PLATE I. ENAMELLED BRONZE SHIELD, THAMES AT BATTERSEA. ($^1/_5$)

[*See* p. 106.

British Museum
Guide to
Early Iron Age Antiquities
1925

R. A. Smith

Anglia Publishing
Watts House
Capel St Mary, Ipswich
Suffolk, IP9 2JB

First published in Great Britain by order of the Trustees of the British
Museum, 1925

This edition published by Anglia Publishing, Ipswich, 1994

Printed in Great Britain by The Ipswich Book Company.

ISBN 1-897874-10-3

Also in this series:
London Museum Medieval Catalogue 1940. ISBN 1-897874-01-4
Victoria and Albert Museum Catalogue of Rings 1930. ISBN 1-897874-02-2
British Museum Guide to Anglo-Saxon Antiquities 1923. ISBN 1-897874-03-0

PREFACE TO SECOND EDITION

CONSIDERABLE alterations have been rendered necessary in this Guide by important additions from Britain and central Europe, and by the removal of the whole collection into a gallery where it now faces the series illustrating the Late Iron Age, described in the *Anglo-Saxon Guide*. During the last twenty years our knowledge has been widely extended by the publication of the late Joseph Déchelette's *Manuel* on this period; and Dr. T. Rice Holmes's *Ancient Britain*, though more historical than archaeological, has proved of the greatest value. Many other writers named in the text have thrown light on the Early Iron Age of several continental countries, and the last papers of the late Mr. E. C. R. Armstrong deal authoritatively with the corresponding period in Ireland.

The new map of Europe involves much relabelling of exhibits and a certain confusion, which may be in part avoided by using the old geographical names for the smaller territories; and in any case modern political divisions have little relation to the distribution of tribes and peoples twenty centuries ago. Some vagueness in dating is still permissible if not essential; and the conspectus which precedes the Introduction will give some idea of the prevalent systems, though it is not to be inferred that corresponding stages of culture were contemporary throughout Europe, much less in Asia and Africa.

The term 'Late Keltic' suggested as a name for the Early Iron Age of Britain and Ireland in 1863 by Sir Wollaston Franks, has been abandoned in this edition because there is some uncertainty as to the existence or date of an earlier Keltic civilization in these islands; and though a Keltic language was spoken in western Europe during the period of La Tène, opinions are still divided as to the language and nationality of the Hallstatt people, whether here or on the Continent.

The Trustees are indebted to the Council of the Society of Antiquaries for permission to use or adapt many of their illustrations; and besides these, six new plates and thirty figures are inserted in the present edition, including one each from Messrs. Bulleid and Gray's *Glastonbury Lake-village*, Mrs. Cunnington's *All Cannings Cross*, and *Altertümer unserer heidnischen Vorzeit*, vol. v (Mainz). With the exception of figures marked with an asterisk (*), all the objects represented belong to the Museum collections; and the scale is indicated where practicable by a fraction, which refers to linear measurement: thus, $\frac{1}{2}$ means that the original has twice the length and breadth, but four times the area of the reproduction. Additional illustrations in postcard form are to be obtained at the Sale counters in the Museum.

The present edition contains much new matter, due to further research and the increase of the collection: like the first, it is the work of Mr. Reginald A. Smith, B.A., F.S.A., Deputy-Keeper of the Department.

O. M. DALTON, Keeper.
Department of British and
Mediaeval Antiquities.

January, 1925.

CONTENTS

LIST OF PLATES

LIST OF ILLUSTRATIONS

HALLSTATT PERIOD

KELTIC EUROPE

SCHUMACHER	DÉCHELETTE	HOERNES
Hallstatt A 1000–800	Hallstatt I 900–700	Early H. (Geometric) 1000–850
Hallstatt B 800–700		Middle H. (Orientalizing) 850–650
Hallstatt C 700–600	Hallstatt II 700–500	Late H. (Early Greek) 650–500
Hallstatt D 600–500		

BOLOGNA

DÉCHELETTE	MACIVER	HOERNES	
1000–90	Benacci I 1050–950	950–750	} Villanova
900–750	Benacci II 950–700	750–600	} Villanova
750–550	Arnoaldi 700–500	600–500	
550–400	Certosa (Etruscan) 5th century	500–400	

GREEK POTTERY

DÉCHELETTE
Proto-Geometric 11th–9th century
Dipylon 9th–8th century
Proto-Corinthian 750–600
Corinthian, &c. 7th century
Attic black-figure 6th century
Early red-figure Late 6th century

LA TÈNE PERIOD

DÉCHELETTE	REINECKE	MONTELIUS (France)	MONTELIUS (Scandinavia)	VIOLLIER (Switzerland)
La Tène I : 500–300	La Tène A : 5th century }	La Tène I : 400–250	Pre-Roman I : 500–300	La Tène I : 450–250
La Tène II : 300–100	La Tène B : 4th century }	La Tène II : 250–150	Pre-Roman II : 300–150	La Tène II : 250–50
La Tène III : 1st century B.C.	La Tène C : 3rd and 2nd centuries B.C.	La Tène III : 150–1 B.C.	Late pre-Roman : 150–1 B.C.	La Tène III = Roman
La Tène IV (Britain) : 1st century A.D.	La Tène D : 1st century B.C.			

INTRODUCTION

In one sense of the term, the civilized world is still in the Iron Age, while in some remote regions that stage of culture has not yet been reached. The use of metallic iron for domestic, agricultural, and military purposes is of long standing in Europe, but in many areas there was evidently a time, to be determined within a century or two, when iron was unknown or unappreciated, and bronze was the staple metal for most purposes of life.

The archaeological theory that, at least in Europe, the invention and working of copper and bronze followed the age of Stone or the Neolithic period, and that the subsequent discovery of iron terminated the use of bronze for many purposes, has been found to work satisfactorily, and to accord with the great majority of recent discoveries. It must, however, be understood that the date at which iron was first worked is not by any means determined, and local conditions no doubt had much to do with its invention. Thus there seems to have been no Bronze Age in Africa, except in Egypt; and in Case K (Prehistoric Room) is exhibited a lump of what is now iron rust which was found wrapped up in a fabric with a mirror and tools of copper belonging to the 6th Dynasty (2700–2500 B. C.). Nor is this an isolated case (*Bronze Age Guide,* p. 172), and the evidence at present available suggests that in Egypt iron was known as early as bronze or copper. The case is different in Europe, where the succession of metals that have given their names to the prehistoric periods can be more easily followed. If iron had been known in Europe much before the end of the Bronze Age, it is most improbable that every trace of it should have disappeared through the action of air and moisture, while iron objects, which are known to be nearly 3,000 years old, have been found in such quantities and in such good condition at Hallstatt and similar sites.

There is nothing in the actual working of iron that necessitates a comparatively late date in the history of civilization: its production is, in fact, one of the simplest metallurgical processes, and the belief that fusion by the application of great heat was necessary is quite erroneous. Prof. Gowland held that the method of iron-smelting in Europe dates only from the seventeenth century; and as the aim of earlier ironworkers was only to produce wrought iron, the metal was always handled in a solid mass, and not as molten cast-iron. The discovery of the art may have been due to the accidental presence of pieces of rich iron ore among the embers of the domestic fire, and these, after reduction to the metallic state, cannot have failed to attract attention and stimulate curiosity. Another possible explanation is that primitive man, having already obtained metallic copper from certain rocks, experimented with others in his rude furnace, and eventually struck on a deposit of ironstone.

More than one discovery has been made in Europe of prehistoric ironworks, but as yet the precise form of the earliest furnace has not been established. Comparison with primitive methods surviving in other countries (as Japan) renders it most probable that the ore was at first reduced in a shallow hole in the ground, the blast being introduced over the edge. At a later date a development is seen in the Adriatic region and central Europe, where this cavity for the furnace was excavated in the steep side of a low bank, an opening being made for the removal of the iron, and the blast introduced at the bottom, either through the same or another opening. It is important to remember that the metal was never smelted, but always obtained from the ore as a solid mass of malleable iron.

Although there are various proofs that iron was produced in Britain centuries before the Roman occupation, no furnaces of the earliest period have been discovered; and it is therefore probable that the ancient Britons employed the simple low hearth resembling the Catalan furnace of the Pyrenees, which has been in use there from very remote times to our own day. The source from which Britain derived the furnace and art of extracting iron from its ores seems to have been the Mediterranean region, either the eastern Pyrenees or north-west Italy; but it may also be reasonably held that the first iron-furnace of the Britons was derived from that used so successfully in the extraction of tin. It is important to notice that two of the earliest sites of ironworks in Europe are situated in the upper Danubian region within easy reach of the famous cemetery of Hallstatt. One is in the neighbourhood of Hüttenberg, in the upper basin of the Drave, Carinthia: the second on another tributary of the Danube, the Mur in Styria. In the Swiss Jura also are extensive remains of ancient ironworks, perhaps somewhat later than those just mentioned, and probably the source of the iron used so extensively at La Tène and other localities in the neighbourhood, before the Roman conquest.

The ornamental use of this metal at a very early date in Egypt is proved by the discovery of iron beads in a pre-dynastic grave at El Gerzeh, 40 miles south of Cairo; and during the 19th Dynasty (about 1350 B. C.) tribute of iron as a rare metal was sent from Syria. Among the Philistines it was known in the twelfth century, and the Bible implies the use of iron in Palestine during the eleventh century.

The Minoan peoples of the Greek islands used the metal for jewellery in what is called the Mycenaean period, and the chief centre in the Levant was undoubtedly Commagene, 'the birth-place of Iron' (*ubi ferrum nascitur*, see *Guide to Greek and Roman Life*, 2nd ed., p. 52), about 200 miles due south of the land of the Chalybes, a people who became famous among the classical Greeks for the excellence of their metal.

There is little doubt that the head-quarters of the early Iron industry of Europe came within the borders of Noricum, a province of the Roman empire corresponding to Styria and Carinthia, and a part of Austria, Bavaria, and Salzburg. It can hardly have been a local invention, and though the date of its inception is approximately known, the route by which the craft reached central Europe has not been determined. The Adriatic would afford an obvious approach from the eastern Mediterranean; but the possibility of transmission through the Balkans from the fabled home of metal-working south of the Black Sea must not be overlooked. Once the art had been learnt, the abundant supplies of the metal in Noricum would create an extensive industry, and certainly led to important conquests and tribal migrations.

Little is known of the political geography of Europe at the dawn of the Iron Age; but there is sufficient authority for Illyrians in the Balkans, Ligurians as far west as the Rhone, and Iberians west of the Rhone and in Spain. Hecataeus of Miletus, writing about 500 B.C., mentions Massilia (the modern Marseilles, a Greek colony founded by the Phocaeans about 600 B.C.) as a city of Liguria adjoining the land of the Kelts, who are mentioned also by Herodotus (about 450–440 B.C.). There is another tradition, preserved by the poet Apollonius of Rhodes (240 B.C.), that as early as the sixth century the Kelts were situated in the Rhone valley and round the lakes of Switzerland and north Italy. These Kelts were known as Gauls, a name by no means confined to the inhabitants of what is now France; and their presence on the northern slopes of the Julian Alps (the later Noricum) intimates the route by which the hosts of Brennus marched southward, by way of Aquileia and Venice, to the sack of Rome in 395 B.C. These Gauls were not only perfect strangers to the Etruscans and Romans, but were equipped with strange weapons; and were called Transalpine to distinguish them from earlier settlers in Lombardy, who were called Cisalpine, and became Roman provincials in 222 B.C. The latter seem to be referred to by Livy, who says the Gauls first crossed the Alps in the time of Tarquinius Priscus, a king of Rome who reigned about 600 B.C. From the description given by Polybius (204–122 B.C.), the Cisalpines were a settled and agricultural people who flourished on the rich soil of the Po valley, and have been by some identified with the Umbrians: whereas the later or Transalpine Gauls, according to the same historian, lived in scattered villages without walls and had none of the comforts of life. Their property took the form of cattle and gold, which were easily movable ; and they set much store by an almost feudal military system, the more powerful among them maintaining each a band of armed retainers pledged to their service. It is possible to recognize here the Nordic warriors in command of Alpine soldiery marching through Europe from end to end in search of plunder, rich lands to settle on, and a share in the luxuries of Mediterranean life.

Evidence for the Keltic invasion of the Iberian peninsula is both historical and archaeological. Himilco, a Carthaginian explorer, sailed round the west coast of Europe as far as Britain and Ireland about 500 B. c. His account is lost, but was turned into Latin verse by Rufus Festus Avienus, who was proconsul of Africa in A. D. 366. This suggests that the Ligurians held northern Spain as well as northern France, and that the Kelts had not yet passed the Pyrenees. On the other hand Herodotus (484–425 B. c.) records that the westernmost Kelts were neighbours of the Cynetes, who are shown by Himilco to have inhabited the south of Portugal. The invasion would therefore date from the first half of the fifth century, and this is in fair agreement with archaeology (p. 80), the Kelts having brought a late Hallstatt culture into the peninsula and eventually settled down among the natives of the north-east as Keltiberians. It is evident that they skirted the Pyrenees on the west, as the Ligurians of the lower Rhone valley seem to have held their ground till about 300 B. c.

Himilco was emulated towards the end of the fourth century B.C. (in the days of Alexander the Great and the philosopher Aristotle) by Pytheas, a Greek of Marseilles, who found a Keltic population on the west coast of Gaul, explored Britain, visited the north of Scotland and the Baltic, and discovered Thule (probably Norway) then regarded as the end of the world. His wonderful observations were disbelieved by many writers who quoted him, and some of the statements attributed to him may be distorted ; but he was apparently the first to mention Britain, and the name has some bearing on the Keltic invasion (pp. 9, 112). How long before his date the island had been occupied by continental peoples speaking one or other dialect of the Keltic language is a question for archaeology to solve, and material is fast accumulating. Opinions are divided on the derivation and application of Cassiteros (Greek for ' tin '), which occurs in Homer and must therefore date from at least the ninth century B. c., though the Homeric poems depict Greek civilization of about 1200. Like several ancient names of the metals (e. g. copper from Cyprus, bronze from Brundisium) this name for tin may have been derived from its place of origin—the islands known as the Cassiterides, instead of the islands being called after the metal exported from them. M. Salomon Reinach holds that the name is Keltic (comparing Cassi-vellaunos, Cassignatus, Veliocasses, &c.), and was given by Kelts living on the west coast of France, where they are not generally thought to have been as early as the ninth century; and the statement of Posidonius (quoted by Diodorus) that it was taken 'through the interior of the Keltic country to the people of Massilia and Narbo' does not necessarily take the traffic back before the sixth century B. C. (pp. 3, 6). Brooches of Italian origin, alleged to have been found in this country, indicate at any rate trade in the Hallstatt period, and certain pottery finds are even more significant (p. 25).

The identity of the Cassiterides has been much discussed, but the tendency now is to regard them as the same as Avienus' Oestrymnides 'rich in metals, tin and lead', and in spite of many difficulties to interpret them as the British Isles, especially as the same poem mentions the Hierni and Albiones as presumably known to Himilco. The Stoic Posidonius, who travelled in Britain about 90 B. C., seems to be the authority for the statement that 'the inhabitants of Belerion were very fond of strangers and civilized in consequence. After smelting and purifying the tin they beat it into masses shaped like knuckle-bones, and carried it to an island off Britain called Ictis, which at low tide was accessible to wagons. Here the merchants bought the metal from the natives and carried it over to Gaul.' Belerion is known to be Land's End, and Ictis is best identified with St. Michael's Mount (not twelve miles distant), which is only an island at high water; but Sir William Ridgeway's contention that Ictis was Vectis (Isle of Wight) was subsequently supported by Clement Reid's demonstration of a former land-bridge across the Solent (now reduced to the Black Rock near Yarmouth). The long land-route is the chief objection to this theory. When this traffic began is uncertain : for instance, M. Salomon Reinach thinks the Phrygians were here about 850 B. C., even before the Phoenicians ; but it seems to have declined in the days of Strabo, who wrote in the first twenty years of our era and enumerates wheat, cattle, gold, silver, iron, skins, slaves, and dogs, as exports from Britain, while ivory bracelets and necklaces, red amber beads and glass vessels were among the imports. For three hundred years before Caesar the east-coast districts of Britain had been given over to agriculture, and trade in various commodities with the Continent was evidently of long standing, coinage being introduced by way of Gaul about 200 B. C. Of the country north of the Thames Caesar can have had little personal knowledge, and his account of the natives and the mining of tin is far from precise ; though his conception of the inland population as aborigines who had been displaced by Belgic immigrants, seems to be very near the truth. While the inhabitants near the Straits were the most civilized and resembled their neighbours of Gaul, most of those inland

B

sowed no corn, but lived on milk and flesh, using skins of animals
for clothing. All these, but presumably not the southerners,
stained their bodies blue to frighten their enemies, wore their hair
long, and shaved all but the upper lip.

Whether the expression 'Keltic tin' was due to the conquest
of Cornwall by Kelts or to their handling of the metal on the
way across Gaul, expeditions at the other end of Europe
display the daring and mobility of these 'barbarians', as the
Greeks called any foreigners whose language they did not under-
stand. It has been argued that the invaders who took over or
put an end to the Mycenaean civilization of Greece came from the
lower Danube. Sir William Ridgeway identifies the Achaeans as
Kelts by their physical characteristics, by their use of iron and
brooches, by their geometric style of ornamentation, and the
practice of cremation ; whereas Prof. Bury holds that the rulers in
southern and central Greece during the fourteenth and thirteenth
centuries B. C. were of Greek stock, or at all events of Greek speech,
and concludes that the North exercised no great influence on the
civilization of the Aegean during that period.

In recent years the spectacle-brooch (fig. 36, no. 3) has been found
in northern Greece and as far south as Sparta, but has been referred,
partly on that account, to the Dorians who, according to tradition,
reached the Peloponnese eighty years after the Trojan war and
were best represented in classical times by the Spartans. The
date indicated would be about 1100 B. C., which suits the brooch-
type better than the thirteenth century, when the Achaean invasion
would have taken place. The fair-haired Achaeans, as Homer
calls them, certainly enjoyed a Cretan (Minoan) civilization at
Mycenae, and under their king Agamemnon took a leading part in
the expedition against Troy (about 1194–1184 B. C.). Whether they
were connected with the Kelts of central Europe is a matter
of opinion ; but the Dorians were evidently of the north European
stock (now called Nordic by anthropologists) from which
sprang the Kelts, Gauls, or Galates, these being now regarded
as synonymous. Ancient descriptions of the racial type are
conflicting and indefinite ; but classical writers generally credited
the Kelt with great stature, fair or reddish hair, and blue or grey
eyes. These characteristics, combined with a long head (with
breadth from 70 to 75 per cent. of its length), distinguish the
Nordic blond from the round-headed Alpine race of central
Europe (with cranial index over 80), and the long-headed but dark
Mediterranean stock. The Keltic type therefore is presumably
North German, Teutonic, or Scandinavian, and at the dawn
of history was located in central Europe between the line Rhone–
Saône–Vosges and the Alps, especially in south-west Germany
north-west of Lake Constance. From that region successive
hordes crossed the upper Rhine and established themselves in

western and central Europe, even invading Italy, Greece, and Asia Minor with varying success.

When or where the first Keltic movement took place is a question not likely to be answered ; but as the second half of the Early Iron Age (named after La Tène) saw the greatest expansion of the Keltic power in Europe, and as the Keltic occupation of the Rhine basin seems to have been uninterrupted for some centuries before that period, it may be supposed that the late Hallstatt culture was also Keltic, and was gradually distributed through most of Europe by that adventurous and conquering race. The early Hallstatt civilization may have been simply Illyrian, though the variation of funeral rites is certainly a difficulty.

Caution is, however, necessary in speaking of a Keltic race or the Keltic language, though both terms are convenient once these limitations are understood. Physical indications are in favour of a northern origin for the people known to classical writers as Kelts, and we have the word of Caesar that Kelts and Gauls were the same people. Though the Latin form Celtae is more familiar than the Greek Keltoi, it is the practice in these Guides to use Keltic for the people and celt for the axe-like implement of stone or bronze common in prehistoric times. There is no real connexion between them, and the difference is emphasized by the spelling adopted. The Keltic people consisted of a number of tribes sometimes acting together but not organized as a nation, and probably including groups of various racial types, loosely connected by a common language. Caesar's division of Gaul into three parts shows that the Keltic element was strongest in the central zone of what is now France ; and it is there that the Alpine race is best represented— short, dark-haired, and extremely brachycephalic (short-headed) with a mean cephalic index of 84. This description does not tally with what is known of the ancient Kelts, and it is now assumed that the dominant people descended from the north or east on the indigenous population of the Alpine region and either settled among them as a ruling caste or recruited them for distant expeditions in search of plunder or territory. The tall fair type has disappeared from what was in Caesar's time Gallia Celtica, probably absorbed by the indigenous dark race, as were the German Franks, who invaded the country centuries later. The Kelts or their predecessors crossed the upper Rhine perhaps as early as 900 B. C. and about 250 B. C. the Belgae, who are known to have been of Teutonic origin, crossed the lower Rhine and founded Gallia Belgica (between the Rhine, the Marne, and the Seine) : they no doubt spoke a dialect of the Keltic language, but their practice of cremation indicates some racial difference from their neighbours in eastern Gaul, though their physical structure either in France or Britain can no longer be determined.

Even though it involved the destruction of the skeleton, cremation is in itself an index of race, and its geographical distribution in Europe is of special interest. It is northern and barbarian, whereas inhumation is oriental and classical; but there are exceptions both in time and place. In the late Bronze Age cremation was general in Europe, and in the Hallstatt period the two rites were practised together in varying proportions: thus at Hallstatt itself the richer graves contained burnt bones, but at Watsch and St. Margaret in Carniola the balance was on the other side, the unburnt burials being the richer and more numerous; and on the Glasinatz plateau in Bosnia, another site of the Hallstatt civilization, inhumations were sixty per cent. of the total and the earliest objects were taken from such graves. At Santa Lucia, Goritz (near Tolmino), where the burials range from the eighth to the fifth century B.C., nearly all were cremated. It may be that cremation was introduced by Keltic invaders of the Ligurian and Illyrian districts where inhumation is known to have been the rule before their appearance on the scene; but burials assigned to the sixth and fifth centuries in the Pyrenees are all incinerations, like the 2,264 dating from the fourth century which were excavated by the late Marquis de Cerralbo between Saragossa and Madrid (Aguilar de Anguita and other sites). In north Italy both rites were practised during the Keltic period, but the body was generally unburnt, as at Giubiasco, though in the neighbouring cemetery of Golasecca nearly all were cremated, and the same rule was observed in the Este and Bologna districts. The contemporary Villanova culture (p. 13) was quite distinct from that of Hallstatt, though it should be noted that cremation, prevalent at the outset of the Iron Age at Hallstatt, in the Bologna district, and in Etruria alike, gradually (but at different rates) gave way to inhumation in all three centres.

The main Keltic area of the Early Iron Age comprised eastern France and southern Germany; and here the dead were buried as a rule unburnt. This practice continued till the middle La Tène period in the Marne (Champagne), but on the Rhine pressure from the north accounts for cremation at an earlier date. Thus the richest graves of La Tène I, such as Waldalgesheim, Weisskirchen, Schwarzenbach, Klein-Aspergle, and even Eygenbilsen in Belgium, contained incinerations with plenty of imported bronze vessels though seldom any arms; but Déchelette observed that the frontier between Keltic unburnt burials and the cremated Germans in the third and fourth centuries B.C. must be drawn a little south-west of Leipzig. Teutonic tribes in the period La Tène I had hardly passed the middle Elbe, but were in occupation of the Main valley when the Cimbri and Teutones were checked by Marius in 102–101, B.C.; and in late La Tène times cremation was general not only in south Germany but also in northern Gaul where the Belgae were now established.

The term Galates is often used for Kelts and Gauls, though Diodorus, who wrote about 50 B. C. (the date of Caesar's conquest of Gaul), said 'the Kelts are those who live in the interior of the country (France) above Marseilles, those near the Alps, and those on the north of the Pyrenees. The people situated above Keltica, who inhabit all the lands extending from the Ocean (Atlantic) and the Hercynian Forest (Taunus to Carpathians) to Scythia, are called Galates. Still the Romans include all these peoples under a common name, and call them Galates without distinction.' Alexandre Bertrand in 1875 concluded, from a close examination of the text of Polybius, that the Galates, although of the Keltic race, were those who lived on the upper Danube and extended to Thrace, the Bosphorus, and Asia Minor (Galatia); whereas the Kelts or Gauls, who were possibly connected with the Umbrians (called *veteres Galli* by Marcus Antonius Gnipho, the Gaulish friend of Caesar and Cicero), founded Cisalpine Gaul in Italy and were, in southern France, the neighbours of the Ligurians. The Galates first appeared in Italy in 390 B. C. and probably led the Senones to the sack of Rome: they, and not the Cisalpine Gauls, were the strangers who alarmed the Etruscans. Perhaps the Galates were the dominant and military element of the Keltic world.

The three names (Galli, Keltae, Galates) must, however, be carefully distinguished from Gael or Goidel, the name of one division of the Kelts, who were distinguished from the Brythons by their language. Of all the Indo-European languages (see *Bronze Age Guide*, 2nd ed., p. 13) Keltic is nearest akin to Italian, and its two main divisions are represented among the ancient languages of Italy. Apart from the question of race, the Keltic-speaking peoples are divided philologically into P Kelts and Q Kelts, the latter being represented in the British Isles by the Gael of Ireland, the Scottish Highlands, and the Isle of Man. This branch of the Keltic language can be traced in Spain and Greece; and the Siculo-Latin dialects which belonged to this group took root in Italy before the southward advance of the P group, comprising the Oscans and Umbrians. Remains of this Goidelic language which retained the Indo-European qv (later k) are rare in western Europe, but Mr. Harold Peake instances the Gaulish Sequani, with their river Sequana (Seine), as a Goidelic reserve where the Hallstatt bronze sword was not superseded by the large iron sword of that period (p. 49). In the Gaulish word *petorritum* (four-wheeled chariot) the numeral corresponds to the Welsh *pedwar*, but the original *qu* is preserved in the Latin *quattuor* (Old Irish *cethir*, Highland Gaelic *ceithir*, and Manx *kiare*). The bronze calendar found at Coligny, Dépt. Ain, in 1897 and dating from the reign of Augustus has names including Q and P elements side by side, the latter being characteristic of Brythonic, which seems to have been the language of Britain when Pytheas of Marseilles visited these shores in the fourth century B. C. It is now held by leading philologists that the Goidelic language was never spoken in what is now England, and the theory of a displacement of the Q Kelts is therefore difficult to uphold ; but it has not yet been shown by what route or from what centre the Goidelic population or language reached Ireland. Its extension to Scotland dates from the fifth century of our era, when Scots from the north of Ireland founded a kingdom in Argyllshire (Dalriada). About the same time (from 450 onwards) P Kelts from south-west England migrated to Brittany to escape the Anglo-Saxon invaders, and the language spoken to-day in some parts of Brittany is similar to Cornish, which became extinct quite recently. As a living language Welsh best illustrates the Brythonic tongue, but except for place-names the earliest records of the language are later by centuries than its introduction into Britain ; and there are no traces of Gaelic or Goidelic till the fifth century after Christ, when names appear in Latin and Ogham characters on the tombstones (*Anglo-Saxon Guide*, p. 120).

The race and language of the Picts are still matters of discussion, one view being that they were non-Aryan aborigines who were thrust into the Highlands of Scotland by Keltic invaders; and a good deal has been made of the fact that inheritance in the female line and a kind of matriarchy existed among them. They are first mentioned in an oration addressed to the Emperor Constantine Chlorus by the rhetorician Eumenius in A. D. 296 ; but an earlier hint is given by the name Britain, which in the form 'Pretanic islands' goes back to the time of Pytheas (p. 4) and is held to be a Welsh or Brythonic rendering of the Goidelic *Cruithne* (the painted people, Latin *Picti*). In this light the Picts may be regarded as the inhabitants of all Britain and Ireland, found here by the Keltic invaders (whether Goidel or Brython) and provided with a Keltic name referring to their painted bodies ; but for this reason the Kelts are more likely to have come as traders and settlers than as hostile invaders. In Asia Minor, for instance, they named the land they conquered after themselves.

Whatever their origin, the small black-haired people of certain parts of Ireland and the Highlands of Scotland, whose ancestors no doubt spoke Erse or Gaelic, must be distinguished racially from the tall Highland Kelts, who answer to the classical description and brought the Keltic language from the Continent during the Early Iron Age. The Teutonic element was less in these Goidelic and Brythonic invaders than in their successors the Belgae, who are known to have crossed the Rhine into northern France (about 250 B. C.), and according to Caesar invaded Britain, ruling on both sides of the Channel. The maritime districts (south-east Britain) were inhabited by people who crossed over from Belgium to plunder and attack the natives, and almost all of them were called after the continental tribes to which they originally belonged.

It is quite in accord with their German origin that the Belgae practised cremation ; and in spite of Ptolemy's evidence that, in the second century of our era, they occupied what is now Hampshire, N. Wilts., and Somerset, it is reasonable to identify them with the makers of the pedestal cinerary urns (Aylesford type, see p. 129), which are abundant in Kent and Essex. It is assumed that the inhabitants of Kent (Cantii) and Essex (Trinobantes) were of the same stock, as the Atrebates (with their capital at Silchester, *Calleva*), who linked them with the West, are known to have been a Belgic tribe ; but, as at present known, the pedestal urn and practice of cremation have a more limited distribution (p. 122). It was these people that Caesar saw most of on his two incursions.

The native military force consisted of infantry and charioteers, but there was perhaps no cavalry in the strict sense. The chariot, as in the time of Homer, took the warrior in and out of the battle, but the fighting was generally on foot. As to the scythed-axles mentioned by Pomponius Mela (about A. D. 45), and Silius Italicus, archaeology is at present silent, though both Tacitus and Lucan (also of the first century) used the same word (*covinnus*) for the British chariot, without referring to the blades on the axles. A thick curved blade, 6 in. long, with a stout tang of quadrangular section nearly 17 in. in length, was found with an iron wheel-tire, a dagger, sickles, tools, and chains, at Bigbury camp, near Canterbury, but was probably the coulter of a plough. A similar iron object has been found in the marsh-village at Glastonbury, and scythe-like blades are known from Ham Hill, Somerset, and Bokerly Dyke, Wilts. ; but no actual scythed wheel has come to light. Caesar, who saw scythed chariots in Pontus in 47 B. C., would hardly have failed to mention any he saw or heard of in Britain. Xenophon mentions 200 scythed chariots in the army of Cyrus, 401 B. C.

Attention has been called by Sir William Ridgeway to armament as an indication of race ; and there are several resemblances between the panoply of warriors buried at Glasinatz (about twenty-four miles east of Serajevo in old Bosnia) and that of the Achaeans before Troy. But the shield generally described in the Homeric poems belongs to the civilization of Mycenae, which was based on that of Minoan Crete, and stood in vivid contrast to the barbarism of central Europe. The elaborate shield of Achilles cannot well be referred to any other culture, and the Achaeans must have been sufficiently Hellenic to carry on the Mycenaean tradition. Least of all can such a work of art be attributed to the Geometric school of design which followed the Mycenaean period. The cumbrous shield shaped like a fiddle-back of Ajax, Hector, and other Homeric heroes, was a circle of hide, bent in to form a waist near the centre, and slung from the shoulder in action. It seems to have given place, at least in Attica, to a rectangular pattern wielded in the hand ; and this, in its turn, was superseded in some parts by the round shield or buckler which, according to Herodotus, was invented by the Carians, and seems to be the pattern referred to in passages added to the Homeric text in the eighth century B. C. The fragment of an Attic vase here illustrated (fig. 1) shows the three shield-forms above mentioned side by side, and warrants the conclusion that in some areas they were practically contemporary. The Boeotian shield, well known from the coinage, is not unlike the ordinary Homeric form, contracted in the centre ; and it should be pointed out in this connexion that such a pattern appears as an ornamental motive on a bronze belt (fig. 2) of the Hallstatt period in Hungary (Case F). This is by no means

*Fig. 1.—Shields from Greek vase, Piraeus. ($\frac{3}{4}$)

the only sign of intercourse between the Mycenaean area and central or even northern Europe (p. 36); and it is worthy of remark that in Epirus Greek and barbarian met for purposes of commerce. Herodotus relates how sacred objects bound up in wheaten straw were brought from the Hyperboreans (of the Baltic) to the Scythians (of the lower Danube and south Russia), the latter forwarding them westward to the Adriatic. The route was then southward till the Greeks received them at Dodona in Epirus, transporting them to the Maliac Gulf and across to Euboea, thence by various stages to the sacred island of Delos.

Classical material of the Early Iron Age is preserved in the Department of Greek and Roman Antiquities; but something must here be said of the style that spread over a large part of Europe and was also adopted or revived in Greece and Italy after the Mycenaean period. This school of art, which knew little or nothing of the naturalistic figure designs of Crete and Mycenae, was characterized by an almost exclusive use of geometric designs, interspersed with friezes of human and animal figures, poorly represented (First Vase Room). The best-known locality for vases and ornaments of this style is the Dipylon cemetery north-west of Athens ; and this stiff and mechanical treatment of ornamental motives is on this account sometimes known as the Dipylon style. Recent excavations have at least rendered it probable that the style was much earlier than is generally held, and was in fact contemporary, though unconnected, with some products of Mycenaean art. Its beginnings in Greece are recognized after 1200 as Proto-geometric, and the true Geometric or Dipylon style began about 1000 B. C.

Ornament of this kind on pottery and bronze-work may indeed be considered as common to a large part of Europe in the Bronze Age ; and it is now correct to consider the Mycenaean culture as a novelty from the south, and the Dipylon school as heirs of the Bronze Age culture of Europe. In Italy, as in Greece, these two distinct currents can be discerned in the remains of the period under review ; and the Geometric style is represented west of the Adriatic by numerous relics that have come down to us from the

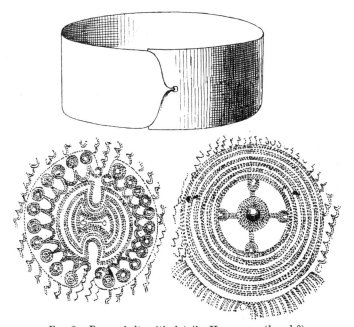

Fɪɢ. 2.—Bronze belt, with details, Hungary. ($\frac{1}{8}$ and $\frac{2}{3}$)

Villanova period. This name is taken from a celebrated cemetery near Bologna in Italy (see table, p. xɪɪ), where the cinerary urns especially exhibited such decorative features as the meander or Greek fret, the swastika or fylfot, the step-pattern, hatched triangles and disconnected rectangles, arranged for the most part in horizontal bands. All these motives occur also at Hallstatt as well as in Greece, and there was probably no great difference in date between similar products in these three principal centres. Prof. Peet holds that the Terramara people moved south after the fall of Cretan power in the Mediterranean, and the general lines of the Early Iron Age civilization in Italy were definitely laid down before the first vases of the Greek Geometric style reached the shores

of Campania and Tuscany.   The Early Iron Age of Italy was
therefore not entirely due to Greek influence: the bucchero ware
for instance was derived from the polished black ware of the
Terremare.

In addition to linear ornament, the employment of human and
animal figures preceded the Iron Age in southern Europe as well
as in Germany and Scandinavia, where contact with the south was
maintained by means of the amber trade.   Shields, for example, of
that period show stamped figures of water-fowl (sometimes only
the fore-part) intermingled with bosses and concentric rings,
while in Italy a further stage had been reached, as exemplified on
the engraved brooches, knives, spear-heads, swords, and discs of the
Villanova period.   During
the bronze sword period at
Hallstatt there seems to have
been no figure decoration, but
the succeeding (iron-sword)
period on that site is richly
represented by articles decorated in the *situla*-style.   Such
is the name given to a method
of ornamenting bronze pails
(Latin *situlae*) by means of
horizontal bands or friezes
containing rows of animals
and men, a method that is
seen in its fullest development in the many examples
found at or near Bologna.
During the Hallstatt period
the *situla*-style, both north
and south of the Alps, shows

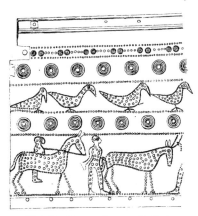

*Fig. 3.—Bronze from pail, Sesto
Calende, Lake Maggiore.   (½)

traces of the early Geometric style of Europe, not only in the survival
of linear patterns but also in technique.   The principal figures have
contour lines, and the dots and bosses of the Bronze Age are still
to the fore, while smaller figures of water-fowl, horses, &c., as
well as concentric rings, are stamped in the bronze (fig. 3).   The
figures were embossed (*repoussé*) by hammering from the back, and
details were added from the same side by means of punches,
which produced bosses of various sizes; while on the front the
figures were outlined by means of a chisel, each blow with the
hammer producing a short line, quite different from the continuous
line of a graving-tool.   A good Italian example of this stage is the
series from the warrior's tomb at Corneto (the ancient Tarquinii)
perhaps before 800 B.C.; and a specimen is given (fig. 3) from
Sesto Calende in the province of Milan, where a richly furnished
burial after cremation is assigned by leading authorities to the

early Hallstatt period, though a short sword with 'horse-shoe' pommel accompanied the helmet and greaves—possibly a relic of the earlier Gaulish invasion alluded to by Livy (p. 3). It may be added that this use of the horse for riding, as shown on this and other pails (such as the Watsch example), no doubt contributed largely to the mobility of the Keltic tribes who roamed over most of Europe at this period. Bronze vessels of the early Hallstatt period were made of sheet metal bent into shape and not soldered but joined by a series of rivets. Solder is said to have been invented by Glaucus of Chios about 490 B. C.

*Fɪɢ. 4.—Lid of pail, Hallstatt, Upper Austria. (about ¼)

*Fɪɢ. 5.—Pail with lid, Hallstatt. (⅙)

A change set in about 700 B. C. when bronze was cast and chased, and Oriental influences are seen in the metal-work of the next two centuries. The centre of distribution has been identified as Este (seventeen miles SW. of Padua), and pails in the new style were traded through the countries lying at the head of the Adriatic, to Bologna on the south and Austria on the north. Through the Ionian Greeks came Oriental motives such as sphinxes, centaurs, and winged quadrupeds, which appear on contemporary Greek pottery ; and here first are scenes represented, many figures being grouped in religious processions, chariot-races, or athletic competitions. To the sixth century are assigned some of the Este series, one from Watsch in Carniola and the cover (fig. 4) of a pail (fig. 5) from Hallstatt, with a stag cropping a plant, a sphinx, a goat holding a branch in its mouth, and a winged lion holding in its jaws, by the foot, the hind-quarters of some animal. ; To the next century belong the Kuffarn pail from lower Austria (reproduction in Greek and Roman Department), and the ornamented sword-scabbard from Hallstatt.   Contemporary with these is the Certosa pail, which is interesting from more than one point of view. A selection from its figures shows (fig. 6) a mounted warrior

*Fɪɢ. 6.   Figures from pail, Certosa, Bologna.

with no shield but the helmet and axe characteristic of the Po valley ; and foot-soldiers with oval shield and Illyrian helmet, or with the Etruscan shield and javelin.   The spade-shaped celt mounted as a throwing axe (perhaps the *cateia*) is better seen in the next figure, and one shows the north Italian hat, and a bundle of spits for the sacrifice, which may be the origin of the bar-currency (p. 165).

The representation of confronted animals, almost heraldic in style, is another indication of contact at some time with the East.   Common in Assyrian art, where it is usually associ-ated with the sacred tree, this motive occurs in widely separ-ated areas, as at Dodona, on a plaque of the fourth century B. C. (fig. 7) ; in south Russia, eighty miles from the sea of Azof, on a gold band (fig. 8) of the early third century ; and on buckets found in south Britain (as fig. 135).   Such are a few instances of artistic borrowing in the ancient world.

*Fɪɢ. 7.—Embossed bronze, Dodona, Epirus.   ($\frac{2}{3}$)

Whether there was any racial connexion between the peoples whose civilization is revealed to us at Hallstatt and La Tène is a question that has been much discussed but not finally settled. It has been contended that in some parts of central Europe (as Bavaria and Styria) the Hallstatt culture persisted down to Roman times and was not affected by the new tendencies apparent in Gaul and the upper Rhine district during the second half of the Early Iron Age in Europe. This contention is no doubt based on the absence of La Tène forms on certain sites occupied by people sharing the Hallstatt culture ; but it is possible that such sites were left untouched by the Kelts of the La Tène period, or were deserted for some centuries before the civilization of Rome found its way across the Alps. One of the best instances of continuous habitation from the Hallstatt to the Roman period

*Fig. 8.—Embossed gold band, Chertomlyk, S. Russia. ($\frac{2}{3}$)

is Velem St. Veits, about sixty miles due south of Vienna. Here scientific excavation has distinguished cultural strata which show how the Hallstatt forms were replaced by those of La Tène, and how the latter passed from stage to stage till the Roman power was felt in this region. It is possible that the Hallstatt folk represent an early advance of the Keltic race into the Danube basin, in much the same manner as the Umbrians preceded the Gauls in northern Italy (p. 9) ; but as the civilization of La Tène presents several important contrasts to that enjoyed by the salt-mining community of the Austrian Tyrol, it would be unwise to date the advent of the true Kelt much before the fifth century B. C. when Hallstatt was in decline. It may well be that the culture of La Tène was introduced by newcomers of pure Keltic blood, who came eastward into the upper Danube area from the Rhine.

The historical sketch given above may serve to explain the distribution of the earliest bronze and other antiquities which illustrate the relations between the classical peoples of the Mediterranean and the 'barbarians' settled beyond their borders in the fifth century before the Christian era.

In the accepted scheme for subdividing the period named after
La Tène, a place is found for the archaic Greek bronzes and
pottery vases that were evidently imported into central Europe,
and found for the most part in the neighbourhood of the upper
Rhine and its tributaries.   Dr. Paul Reinecke, of Mayence, does
not treat this phase as a transition period from 'Hallstatt' to
'La Tène', but gives it an independent existence as his period *A*.
Following on this is the century during which native art, inspired
by classical models, began to show a decided individuality, the old
motives appearing in a debased form more adapted to the Keltic
technique.   Dr. Otto Tischler called this the *Early* period of La
Tène (La Tène I), which corresponds to period *B* of Dr. Reinecke's
system.   Subsequent changes, to be noticed elsewhere, marked the

*Fig. 9.—Frieze from the old Parthenon, Athens.

remaining periods of La Tène, the *Middle* and *Late* La Tène
of Dr. Tischler running parallel to periods *C* and *D* of Dr. Reinecke
(table, p. xii).

Apart from the cemeteries of north Italy, which were evidently
used by the Kelts, the area most affected by the culture of La
Tène comprises a broad strip from the north of France through the
Champagne district, the Meuse, Moselle and Saar valleys, Lorraine,
Alsatia, Würtemberg, Franconia, Bavaria, Bohemia, and upper
Austria.   The limits are approximately Great Britain and the
Carpathians, the Alps and the central mountain-chain of Germany.
Of this area the eastern half, comprising eastern Bavaria, the
upper Danube valley, the Styrian Alps, and Bohemia, contains
many remains clearly connected with the Venetian culture of the
Adriatic.   Whether the inhabitants of this area were connected
through Hungary with the Scythians of south Russia is not at
present clear, but it is evident that the head-quarters of the La Tène
style must be looked for farther west ; and the finest products of
the period are found to be concentrated in southern Germany and
north-east France, the actual centre of radiation for such objects
being apparently the middle Rhine.

The second part of the Early Iron Age is now generally
believed to begin in the fifth century (500 or 450 B. C.) and the stage
known as La Tène I (p. 51) is well represented by the Morel

collection from the Champagne area of France.   Like the preceding stage (late Hallstatt) it derived much of its artistic quality from Italo-Greek sources, and the scroll pattern which developed in Switzerland and culminated in Britain just before the Roman conquest is clearly derived from classical art, Greek trade in the West having largely contributed to this result after the foundation of Massilia (Marseilles) about 600 B. C.

*Fig. 10—Pail with detail, Waldalgesheim, Coblenz.

Without attempting to trace the descent of the Greek palmette (Gk. *anthemion*) from the Egyptian lotus-plant, we must go back to the fifth century B. C. for several motives employed in the La Tène period of Europe.   The inquiry is one of interest, as it links the art of pre-Roman Britain to that of the Periclean era ; and, though an anti-climax was inevitable, there is a consummate mastery of design in the Thames shield (pl. I), for example, that makes a comparison with Greek ornamentation at its best by no means ridiculous.

A convenient starting-point is found in the decoration of the old Parthenon on the Acropolis at Athens, which was destroyed by the Persians under Xerxes in 480 B. C.   Some remarkable fragments 'have been recovered from the ruins, and one painted frieze (fig. 9) shows the drooping palmette alternating with the lotus-bud (in developed form), while the stiff palmette (as fig. 53) was also freely employed on the building, in association with the other form which has been sometimes assigned to a later date. That the barbarian artist had the opportunity, but not the power, of copying the drooping palmette is suggested by its occurrence on a pail (fig. 10) of Greek manufacture which was found in the same grave as the flagon (fig. 11)at Waldalgesheim, a gold torc being found at the same place and time, on a slightly higher level.   There is at first sight little connexion between the designs on these three objects, but fig. 12 gives the intermediate stage of the development, or rather degradation, of the palmette.   At the top may be discerned a single leaf of the fan-shaped palmette, springing from the wedge that fills the angle of the volutes.   The volutes take the usual form of S-shaped scrolls, and have the swollen terminals that often occur on Greek vases (fig. 13) during the period of decline (after 330 B. C.).   The naturalistic sprays and rosettes of the Greek pail are also reproduced in an eccentric manner on the torc, while at the base of the triangle may be seen the three-membered motive that seems to have specially attracted the Keltic artist

*Fig. 11.—Flagon with details, Waldalgesheim.

*Fig. 12.—Details of gold torc, Waldalgesheim. ($\frac{2}{3}$)

Fig 13.—Palmette from Greek vase, Nola (F. 129). ($\frac{1}{4}$)

Fig. 14.—Enclosed palmette, from vase, Cyprus (C 871). ($\frac{1}{2}$)

(figs. 175, 102). The two friezes on the torc show a further stage of debasement: the lower one, however, still retains a clear trace of the enclosed palmette familiar in classical art (fig. 14), while the comma-shaped fillings of the angles are clearly a survival of the tear-shaped pendants from the conventionalized lotus-flower of Egyptian ornament. The alternate palmettes of the frieze are inverted ; but this is not unprecedented, and it is clearly from this design that the upper frieze is derived. Thus on the same object may be distinguished three stages in the logical development of Keltic ornament, and this should suggest caution in dating antiquities of this kind merely by analysis of the ornament. The caution is all the more necessary in this case, as the same motive occurs on British work (as fig. 126) of a much later period.

From the classical point of view, a still lower level is reached by the flagon (fig. 11) included in the Waldalgesheim find. Apart

*Fig. 15.—Details of spear-head, Thielle, Switzerland. (¼)

from the form of the vessel, with its tubular spout replacing the open runnel of the classical pattern (fig. 53), the engraved bands of decoration bear but the slightest relation to the palmette, and it is clear that even in the fourth century component parts of certain classical motives had been arbitrarily selected and rearranged in unmeaning combinations. The present example shows the scroll and its peculiar thickening, that were destined to play an important part in Early British art.

Another favourite motive may here be analysed, and examples adduced to show the stages of its evolution. The circle bisected by two semicircles of half its diameter, $\ominus$, is a well-known Chinese symbol (*Yang-yin*), but in the Early Iron Age it seems to be a derivative of the Greek palmette. Perhaps the strongest evidence for this is afforded by the spear-head (fig. 15) from Thielle, now in Berne Museum. At the base of the central triangle may be seen two heart-shaped forms that bear a strong resemblance to the enclosed palmette of the Greek world (fig. 14) ; and if one side of the enclosed design be viewed in conjunction with the central lobe, a possible genesis of the curl flanking the triangle on this blade becomes apparent. It should, however, be pointed out that on the embossed gold disc (fig. 16) from Auvers (Seine-et-Oise) the same motive occurs, but may have been compounded in this instance of a side lobe of the palmette and the space of similar shape between itself and the S-curve that bounds the triple-lobed palmette. Something of this kind is seen on a vase from Cameiros

C

(fig. 17) belonging to the best period of Greek art, where a palmette of seven lobes is flanked by two scrolls, resembling a lyre. It is not contended that one design was derived from the other, only that at a time when classical motives were becoming common property, the same treatment of the palmette may have occurred alike to the vase-painter in Rhodes and the goldsmith in Gaul.

Another Keltic transformation of the classical palmette may here be noticed, and there will be little difficulty in recognizing

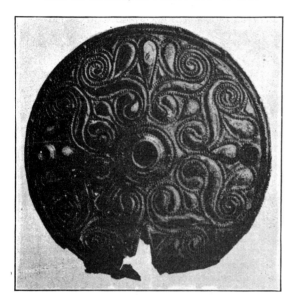

the prototype. Unfortunately nothing is known about the discovery of the cheek-piece (fig. 18) of a helmet (Case 8), but the style of its decoration suggests the fifth century B.C., contemporary with the Schwarzenbach find (p. 24) which included a gold open-work

FIG. 16.—Gold disc and unit of design, Auvers, Seine-et-Oise. ($\frac{2}{3}$)

ornament of a very similar design (fig. 19). The cheek-piece is of a form not unusual at the period, and was probably made between the Balkans and the upper Rhine. The arrangement of the palmette-lobes is here governed to some extent by the shape of the bronze, which was no doubt originally of a golden colour, while the iron studs would be polished like silver.

Enough has been said to show that the ornament gives some clue to the date of Iron Age antiquities, but a more solid foundation for chronology is afforded by the successive changes undergone by the sword and the brooch in Keltic lands. Though typology may here again be sometimes at fault, their contemporary variations are fairly established by numerous discoveries of these two important articles in association. The pioneer in this inquiry was the

FIG. 18.—Cheek-piece of helmet, with iron bosses. ($\frac{2}{3}$)

FIG. 17.—Palmette from vase,
Cameiros, Rhodes (E 99). ($\frac{2}{3}$)

*FIG. 19.—Detail of open-work,
Schwarzenbach, Birkenfeld. ($\frac{2}{3}$)

late Dr. Otto Tischler, of Königsberg; and a summary of his
results is given below (p. 51), with certain modifications and
additions.

In a comprehensive survey of the culture of La Tène published
by Dr. Paul Reinecke in 1902, the principal characteristics of the

c 2

various stages are enumerated ; and the semi-classical era of central Europe, which is represented in the Museum collection by the Somme Bionne chariot-burial (Cases 15, 16), is shown to have left us many important works of art. Greek bronzes, comprising tripods, beaked flagons (as fig. 53), flat round bowls with or without handles, pails and two-handled jars (*stamnoi*), are occasionally found in graves north of the Alps, associated with painted pottery made before 460 B.C. These occur for the most part in richly furnished graves on either bank of the upper Rhine, though similar finds have been made in the valleys of its tributaries, the Moselle (with the Saar) and the Meuse. Dürkheim (thirteen miles west of Mannheim), Schwarzenbach (Birkenfeld in Oldenburg), and Weisskirchen (near Merzig, on Saar, about twenty miles south of Trèves) are typical sites for Greek work of the fifth century B.C., as the painted bowl from Klein-Aspergle (Ludwigsburg, eight miles north of Stuttgart), which must be contemporary with the Somme Bionne example (Case 16), was dated by Professor Furtwängler between 470 and 480 B.C. It is of course possible that these fragile vessels were not buried for some years after their manufacture or importation, but it is barely conceivable that several of the kind should have been in actual use long before they were placed in the tomb. There need be little hesitation, therefore, in dating the burials by the vases ; and the typical grave at this time was a large mound of varying height containing the unburnt body, though surface-graves had here and there already made their appearance.

This chronology is confirmed by the style in which the beaked flagons are ornamented. Below the handle is generally to be seen a stiff palmette (fig. 53), which on the whole preceded in Greek art the drooping palmette (fig. 13). The latter became popular in the fifth century B.C., and is well seen on the Parthenon (finished in 438 B.C.). Barbarian imitations, or adaptations of articles exported from Greece or Italy about that time, are obviously contemporary with the models, as they display peculiarities of style that soon disappeared from the artistic world of the Mediterranean. The distribution of such semi-classical products is more likely to have been by sea from central Italy (Cumae and Capua) than from the Greek city of Marseilles via the Rhone valley.

Native industry during this early phase (La Tène *A*) is best represented by short swords, contrasting with the enormous weapons of the Hallstatt period ; and by tall, conical helmets of bronze, which certainly resemble some Assyrian and later Oriental specimens but are now considered to be exaggerated copies of the contemporary Italian type (almost hemispherical with a knob on the top). Casts of the two best-known Keltic helmets from France are exhibited in Case 26.

As the succeeding periods of La Tène civilization will be conveniently dealt with in describing the Cases containing specimens typical of each, it will only be necessary to say a few words, by way of introduction, concerning Keltic art as it flourished in Britain. On this side of the Channel the Keltic artist was unsuccessful with figure-subjects but was a master of line ; and his gradual divergence from classical models towards eccentric scroll-work of his own fancy can be appreciated by comparing the two bronze shields in Cases 32 and 33—that from the Witham (figs. 113–15) preserves the palmette in a form easily recognizable and has studs of coral from the South ; the Battersea masterpiece (frontispiece) has no obvious relation to classical art, and is decorated with the enamel 'made by barbarians that dwell in Ocean' (p. 102). In the interval between them British art had proved that it could stand alone.

Ceramic art is now known to have developed locally, and a marked improvement on late Bronze Age ware is noticed in recently discovered groups that go back perhaps to the Hallstatt period in Britain. Much of the best discovered by Mr. Bushe-Fox at Hengistbury, Hants (fig. 87), was no doubt imported, but the red ware found by Rev. Walter Budgen at Eastbourne has parallels in the Hallstatt series of southern Germany and was certainly fired on the spot. Farther west, on the Sussex Downs near Cissbury, Mr. Garnet Wolseley has excavated hitherto unsuspected types of pottery (fig. 85) from dwelling-sites, perhaps of the same period ; while the vast collection published by Mrs. Cunnington from an occupied site near Devizes (fig. 86) is assigned to the fifth century B.C. and, like Dr. Clay's series (also in that museum) from Fifield Bavant, has technical merits as well as a most important bearing on our earliest Iron Age. All these differ essentially from what was formerly considered the only British ware of the period. The urn-fields at Aylesford and Swarling in Kent have furnished several complete pottery vessels of types well represented on other early British sites, as at Hitchin (fig. 184) and Shoebury, which we may now look on as of Belgic manufacture, inspired no doubt by Gaulish models, but firmly established in the south-eastern counties. In spite of the variety of forms (fig. 142) there are certain unmistakable features that show their original derivation from prototypes of metal ; nor are bronze vessels of the requisite outline far to seek. In dealing with Aylesford, Sir Arthur Evans has traced the descent of the cordoned vases like fig. 142, nos. 1, 5, from a north Italian type, and an illustration is given to show how close is the resemblance. The Este specimen (fig. 20) has the angular shoulder (*caréné*) which can be readily produced in bronze, but is difficult to render in a less rigid medium such as clay. There are, however, in the Morel collection (Cases 65–74) several examples of thin black pottery, in which this feature is specially noticeable (pl. VI, nos. 7, 12), while others of ruder construction in buff or red ware exhibit a decline in handicraft (pl. VI. nos. 13, 9).

A more natural form for pottery is that of a cordoned vessel from Certosa. The angularity of bronze has given place to a graceful curve, corresponding to that of several Aylesford specimens, while the old tradition is kept alive by the rows of bronze studs now purely decorative. The frieze on the Este specimen is noticed elsewhere (p. 15), and its appearance on vessels of this type shows that the form had taken root in north Italy, even if the parent stock is not to be sought in that region. From the plains of the Italian provinces of Emilia and Venetia the pedestal urn can be traced across Europe and the

*Fig. 20.—Bronze pail with frieze, Este, N. Italy. ($\frac{1}{10}$)

Channel to the south of England ; and there are certain indications that the type was preserved through several centuries. There can be little doubt that the trade-route along which it passed ran for some distance parallel to the Rhine, and it is in the Dépt. Marne (the Champagne) that most examples occur (fig. 64). These can be ascribed without much hesitation to La Tène I, but later relics of the Gaulish period are scarce in that area (pp. 72, 78), and subsequent developments must be sought elsewhere. That from Saint Audebert (fig. 21), which was used as a cinerary urn, and others from the lower Seine district (figs. 22, 23) show that this class of pottery survived the disturbances which revolutionized the funeral rites of Gaul, and connect the urn-fields of south-east Britain with the richer tombs of the Italian plains.

Nor is the cordoned vase the only link that binds the civilization of early Britain to that of classical lands. Aylesford again demands attention, for in the principal burial of that cemetery (fig. 134) there were in addition bronze vessels of classical manufacture, and a more barbaric production in the form of a bucket, the bronze ornamental mounts of which betray classical influence (fig. 135). The effect of imitation during two or three centuries may be appreciated by comparing an Etruscan *cista* of the fourth century (fig. 24) with the Aylesford bucket (fig. 135) of the first century B.C. The first thing to be noticed is the absence from the latter of the heavy solid castings that form the feet and handle-attachments of the classical specimen. Such work was beyond the range of the British artificer, who was never successful with the human or animal form (figs. 158, 159) ; but there is an evident desire to reproduce the salient features of the prototype. The solid uppermost band of the Etruscan specimen is represented by a thin embossed strip at Aylesford, while the classical motives are woefully caricatured. Minor analogies are noticed later (p. 126), but the degradation of the ornament may

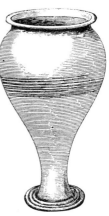

*Fig. 21.—Cinerary urn, St. Audebert, Dépt. Aisne. (⅛)

*Fig. 22.—Cordoned urn, Moulineaux, Rouen. (⅙)

*Fig. 23.—Urn with cover, Hallais, Seine-Inférieure. (⅙)

fitly be dwelt on here, as showing the limitations and at the same time the originality of the native craftsman.

Another remarkable bucket was found containing burnt human bones near Marlborough, Wilts., about 1807, and is now preserved in Devizes Museum. It evidently belongs to the same class and period as the Aylesford specimen, but from certain details of the ornament Sir Arthur Evans concludes that it was made in Armorica and imported from the opposite coast, like many of the Armorican

Fig. 24.—Etruscan bucket, Offida, Picenum (Cat. no. 650). $(\frac{1}{4})$

or Channel Islands type (p. 166) found in Devon and Hants. The sea-horses that occur on the uppermost zone are a conspicuous feature on coins of the Cenomani (Maine) and Redones (Rennes), both of which tribes were located near the Veneti in Gaul, the great sea-faring people of Caesar's time who commanded the mouth of the Loire.

In the description of the objects themselves enough will be found to establish the unique character of native art before the legions of Claudius began the conquest of our larger island. It must, however, be stated at once that Keltic methods and traditions continued in Scotland and Ireland while the Roman province of Britain was being permeated with the civilization of Italy. Early British art as practised in Scotland and Ireland should, in fact, be regarded as the outcome of some centuries of development in what is now south-eastern England : a simple proof of this is the virtual restriction of pre-Roman coinage to an area south of a line from the Bristol Channel to the Wash. The south-eastern area, including the Thames valley, Kent, and the eastern counties, was the cradle of Early British art, the continental parentage of which is now acknowledged. Even if other districts proved more prolific in bronzes, there can be little doubt that this extraordinarily attractive style of ornamentation was focussed in the home counties, and was dissipated by the Roman arms. There are some indications of an artistic revival in the same area after the Roman officials of the province withdrew, early in the fifth century, and remains of that period in England are considered in connexion with Anglo-Saxon antiquities. There is as yet no satisfactory chronology for similar antiquities from other parts of the British Isles, and it is quite likely that some objects exhibited in Cases 24, 25 belong to the fifth or sixth century of our era ; but as the number involved is very limited, all are considered as belonging to the Early Iron Age of Britain.

DESCRIPTION OF CASES

THE northern half of the Iron Age Gallery is devoted to antiquities dating before the birth of Christ, those of the Late Iron Age (the Anglo-Saxon period in England) being on the south side. The western half illustrates foreign series arranged according to countries, and the Early British collection is at the east end. Specimens from Hallstatt itself will be first described, as they are typical of the first half of the Early Iron Age, and occupy the first few Wall-cases and part of Table-case F adjoining.

The Hallstatt cemetery lies in a defile of the Noric Alps (Austrian Tyrol), not far from the village, which is situated on a lake of the same name. From time immemorial this has been the scene of extensive salt-mining, and, though not on one of the ancient highways of commerce, was within forty miles of Noreia, which gave its name to Noricum and is generally considered one of the earliest centres of iron-working in Europe. It is naturally connected with the Danube basin, and was placed by the late Prof. Hoernes on the border of his western and middle-eastern provinces of the Hallstatt culture ; but it was more allied to the West, and, being a rich site, produced some forms which are not found elsewhere.

Both cremation and inhumation were practised on this site and at the same period ; but it was noticed that the burnt subjects belonged to the wealthier or dominant class. Thus iron lance-heads were generally found with skeletons, whereas all but one of the swords and most of the bronze weapons, vessels, embossed plates, shield-bosses, large spirals, and brooches with pendants were found with cremated remains. The cemetery was systematically excavated by Ramsauer between 1846 and 1863 ; and several specimens, acquired on the spot by Sir John Lubbock (the first Lord Avebury) in 1869, are exhibited in Cases 1–3, the most important being the bronze bucket (like fig. 25: *cista*, as opposed to *situla*, fig. 5) of an Italian type found in various parts of Europe, but rarely at Hallstatt itself. A good parallel came from the Monceau-Laurent tumulus at Magny-Lambert, Côte d'Or, and was assigned by Déchelette to the close of the long iron-sword period, about the date of the Warrior's tomb at Corneto (Tarquinii in Etruria), which belongs to the eighth or late ninth century B. C.

Another Hallstatt vessel of the cist type (fig. 26) is of later date and different origin, as the pattern lasted into the period of La Tène (fifth century B. C.) and was produced wholesale in north-east Italy (Venetia) for export to Europe; it is therefore widely diffused and even reached Britain (p. 91). The body is formed of a bronze plate bent into a cylinder and riveted down the side: the base is ornamented with concentric bands or rings in relief, and the twin handles rest on the rim when not in use. The earliest may date from the seventh century, as one was found at Hallstatt with a long iron sword, here as generally elsewhere the burial being after cremation. Specimens have been found in

*Fig. 25.—Bucket with broad hoops, Hallstatt. (⅕)

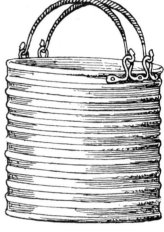

*Fig. 26.—Cordoned bucket, Hallstatt. (¼)

north-east France, Belgium, Germany, and Hungary, but the handles are generally fixed on the side south of the Alps.

The chronology of the Hallstatt period has been much discussed and estimates are given in the table on p. XII. The dates do not apply to all the European areas in which remains of this culture have been discovered, but there is general agreement as to the sequence on the site itself, and the swords are recognized as the best criterion. Stages in the evolution of this weapon during the Early Iron Age are illustrated by original specimens and casts in Case F. The earliest phase is one of transition from the Bronze Age, when bronze swords of three types were in use—the *antennae* type (fig. 27), the Ronzano type (similar, but with an angular expansion in the middle of the grip), and the leaf-shaped sword (with notches and milling at the base of the blade, uppermost in fig. 28). At first iron was scarce and valuable, but its cutting edge was quickly appreciated, and sometimes the blade was

of iron while the bronze tang remained (as fig. 28, middle), the
pommel meanwhile increasing in size to counterbalance the larger
blade that the use of iron made possible and desirable ; and
the limit was reached in the large iron sword period (eighth
century B. C.).   The lowest example in fig. 28 shows this stage

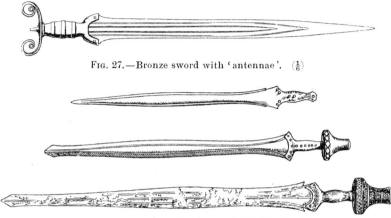

FIG. 27.—Bronze sword with 'antennae'. ($\frac{1}{6}$)

*FIG. 28.—Bronze and iron swords, Hallstatt. ($\frac{1}{4}$)

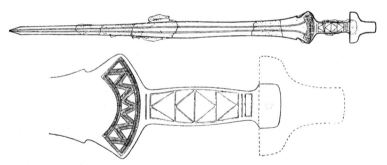

FIG. 29.—Iron sword with gold-foil, Hallstatt. ($\frac{1}{10}$ and $\frac{1}{3}$)

with angular point, ivory pommel, and pronounced notches above
the grip which Mr. Parker Brewis has explained as leaving a
blunted space on either side of the blade for a finger-rest (*ricasso*),
as in Italian swords of the Middle Ages.   Remains of a typical
sword once decorated with gold-foil can be restored as in fig. 29.
    In the seventh century this huge weapon went out of fashion,
and was replaced by the short sword with horse-shoe pommel
(fig. 30) and the knife with fish-tail scabbard (fig. 31).   A similar

chape is seen on a short sword (fig. 32 *e*) of which the blade and scabbard are missing, and a degenerate form entirely of iron is also illustrated (fig. 32 *d*), with the pommel reduced to three studs on a cross-bar, this last type being common in Spain. A bronze dagger is exhibited (probably from Hallstatt) with a plate of iron attached as an ornament to the base of the blade; and the 'anthropoid' sword (fig. 58), a subsequent development of La Tène date, has an obvious relation to fig. 30.

Spear-heads have a leaf-shaped blade and socket for the shaft which is secured by a peg (fig. 32 *f*); and the axe-head might have been used both as a tool and weapon, though the spade type is more

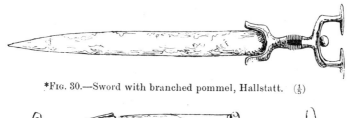

*Fig. 30.—Sword with branched pommel, Hallstatt. ($\frac{1}{5}$)

*Fig. 31.—Dagger with chape, Hallstatt. ($\frac{1}{4}$)

usually represented as a weapon on the embossed pails (fig. 6). The socketed iron celt (fig. 32 *a*) is also found in Britain (fig. 82), but the flat type with trunnions (fig. 32 *b*), of which several iron specimens are exhibited from Hallstatt, is always of bronze in the British Isles.

Bronze bracelets are of various forms in the Hallstatt period: a large specimen of 'nut' pattern is said to have been found near Naples, and part of a smaller one comes from Hallstatt itself, a section being hinged so as to admit the wrist. There is a series with regular lobes (fig. 33) more or less pronounced; and sometimes a plain tube was used for the arm as well as the neck, a good example of the latter coming from the large barrow of Wolfegghof, Buchheim, near Sigmaringen. Anklets (fig. 34) were also common and can be recognized by their oval outline and the bend across the middle. Pins are of bronze with a row of mouldings near the head like a string of beads (fig. 32 *g, h*); and the largest (*j*) is no less than 16 in. long and has a point-protector. The type is not unlike a series from France (Bronze Age Gallery, Case E) in which a length of 2 ft. is frequently exceeded. Among the

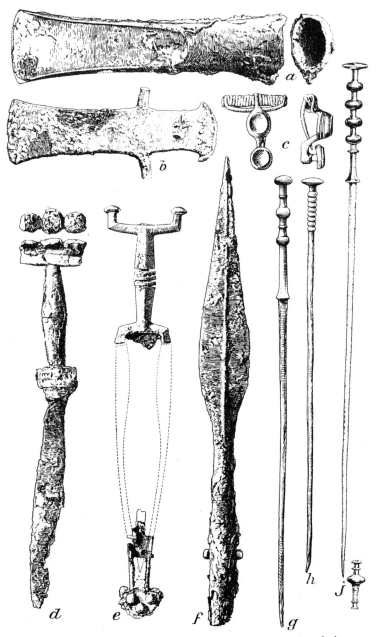

FIG. 32.—Iron celts, daggers, and spear-head, bronze brooch and pins,
Hallstatt. ($\frac{1}{3}$. c $\frac{2}{3}$)

ornaments should also be mentioned the amber beads (fig. 35) which were due to the proximity of Hallstatt to the trade route across Europe by which amber was taken south from the Baltic.

Reference has already been made to bronze-plate working in this period (p. 14), and pieces of two belts are exhibited from

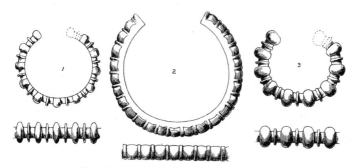

Fig. 33.—Bronze bracelets, Hallstatt. ($\frac{1}{3}$)

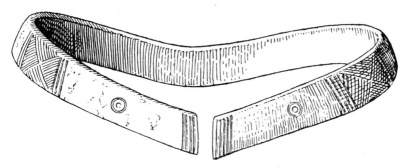

Fig. 34 —Bronze anklet, Hallstatt. ($\frac{1}{4}$)

Hallstatt, one with bosses hammered up from the back, the other with hemispherical bosses fixed to the front by a central pin. There is also a neatly executed panel with seven rows of small bosses each in a ring, separated in the middle row by groups of three vertical lines. There are various forms of belt-clasps ; a boss with triangular pendants attached to the rim by chains, and the bronze cover of a vessel $9\frac{1}{2}$ in. across.

Certain stages and tendencies have been noticed in the ornamentation of bronze vessels at Hallstatt and contemporary sites. First there is the purely geometric style, lightly engraved without embossing. This is followed by another style, seen on many of the broad belts of thin bronze plate from Hallstatt, which have bosses of various sizes and embossed linear ornament, sometimes with rude stamped figures of men, birds, and horses. This is exemplified on the well-known shield found at Halland, Sweden. A third style has been connected with Mycenaean art, and consists of grouped bosses of various sizes as before, but outlined and connected by double or triple dotted and engraved lines. It is to this style that the Hungarian bronze belt (fig. 2) exhibited in Case F must be referred ; and it may be observed that the design on

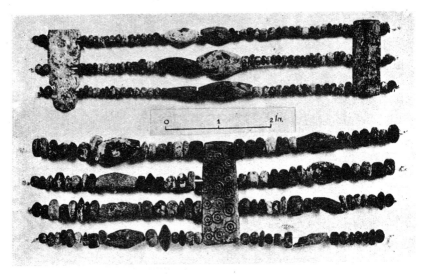

FIG. 35.—Amber beads with bone plates, Hallstatt.

bronze bucklers found in Coveney Fen, Cambs., and in Achmaleddie Moss, Aberdeenshire, bears a close resemblance to the ribbon pattern seen on several Mycenaean works of art. The inference is that even as far north as Britain the Mycenaean civilization found its way (p. 5), the intermediaries being possibly Phoenician traders. A later phase at Hallstatt shows Oriental influence, and has already been touched on in connexion with figure-ornament (p. 15).

By comparing Hallstatt with St. Lucia (Goritz) and St. Michael (Carniola), Dr. Hoernes was enabled to classify the brooches and other typical remains of the Hallstatt period. The earlier series of brooches comprise the ' spectacle '-type with spiral coils of wire (fig. 36, no. 3) or with discs representing those coils (fig. 37) ; and the crescent type (fig. 36, no. 4) with chain-pendants. These are generally distinct from the later series, which includes the Certosa type (fig. 41), serpentine (by-form of fig. 40, IV e), cross-bow (fig. 36, no. 5), and animal (fig. 36, no. 1) brooches. Of the other Hallstatt brooches illustrated, those with spiral discs (nos. 2, 3) are found in Italy, though the double or spectacle-form (no. 3) is practically confined to the south of the peninsula, and is now definitely associated with the Dorian invaders of Greece, as examples have been excavated at Sparta, dating probably 1050–950 B.C.

Animal-brooches (no. 1) are referred to by Homer, and the crescent form with chains and pendants should be compared

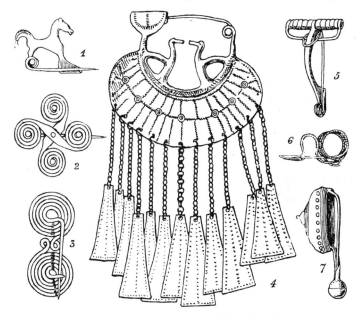

*Fig. 36.—Bronze brooches, Hallstatt. ($\frac{1}{2}$)

with specimens in the Aegina treasure (Gold Ornament Room) which is of late Mycenaean date (1200–1000 B.C.). A compound brooch (no. 5) has the bow and spiral spring not in one piece, and the coil is strengthened by an axis. The drum-shaped brooch (no. 7) is more frequent in the kettle-drum variety (fig. 32 c), which was one of the late Hallstatt forms taken by the Kelts into Spain (p. 81). No. 6 may well be one of the prototypes of the early La Tène type (fig. 49), but authorities differ as to the influence of the Certosa type (fig. 41) on subsequent developments of the brooch.

Pottery shows an enormous improvement both in form and technique, and the best period (eighth and seventh centuries) produced polychrome pieces of surprising dimensions and excellence. The combination of colours (here only red and black) with incised geometric patterns is best seen on the series of platters from Degenfeld and other sites in Würtemberg (pl. II), but the same decoration is often found on large urns, of which plain examples are exhibited in Case 3. The largest (fig. 38) gives some measure of the potter's skill, as the diameter is no less than 21 in., with the surface blackened with graphite and grooved both vertically and horizontally. It was found containing thirteen vessels, of which seven are illustrated (fig. 38), in the sixth Degenfeld barrow at Ebingen, Würtemberg, where the cremated remains had been covered with a heap of stones ; and the group may represent a household set of the early Hallstatt period. They are dated by Dr. Paul Reinecke between 1000 and 850 B. C., but resemble the Gündlingen series attributed by Dr. Schumacher to the eighth century. The gaily-coloured wares belong to the next stage, and three specimens, also from the Edelmann collection, are illustrated on pl. VI, nos. 1–3.

FIG. 37.—Brooch derived from quadruple spiral, Hallstatt. ($\frac{1}{2}$)

There are also flat dishes, pot-lids, and small bowls of black ware, sometimes with a 'kick' (*omphalos*) in the centre like several shown from Saxony in Case 4. The indentation is frequently shallow and saucer-shaped, and appears also as an ornamental device on German (and British) pottery of the period. It is a leading characteristic of Group III in the following list, which gives the sequence for most of northern Germany, according to Dr. A. Voss, of Berlin.

I.   Lausitz type (Lusatian), chiefly in parts of Saxony, Brandenburg, Silesia, but also widely distributed between the river Theiss in Hungary and the Rhine, dating from the late *Bronze* Age.

II.   Aurith, south of Frankfurt-on-Oder : this superseded the Lusatian type and spread from Posen westwards, its earliest examples dating from the *Hallstatt* period.

III. Göritz, north of Frankfurt-on-Oder : occupied a zone north of the Aurith type, including Pomerania and north-east Brandenburg ; also of the *Hallstatt* period.

IV.   Billendorf (Sorau, Lower Lausitz) type occupied a large area

PLATE II. TWO POTTERY PLATTERS FROM WÜRTEMBERG. ($^1/_5$)

[*See* p. 38.

between those of the Aurith and Hallstatt types, and was perhaps influenced by *Villanova* types from North Italy.

Most of the German pottery is exhibited in the Bronze Age Gallery, where the Lusatian series properly belongs; but specimens of the later groups (fig. 39) are shown in Case 4 from Saxony (Klemm collection), and a few words will give the leading features of the four divisions named above. The late Bronze Age ware (I) has grooves, straight or curved, and bosses pressed out from the inside and often enclosed in concentric semicircles (the multiple arch). The paste is generally light or yellowish brown, well made in a

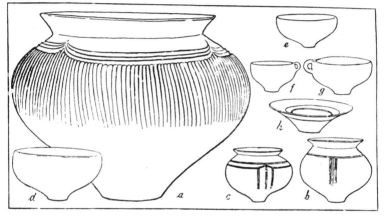

Fig. 38.—Urn found containing other vessels, Degenfeld, Ebingen. (⅛)

great variety of shapes. In the Hallstatt period there is a falling off in most respects: the Aurith series (II) has incised lines (not broad grooves) often accompanied by rows of dots, and includes a bi-conical urn and the saucer with *omphalos* base (p. 38). In Group III a frequent ornament consists of shallow circular depressions (cupules) in lines or groups (already referred to) and incised chevrons are frequent on the bulge: 'face-urns', a type common in E. Germany and ranging from the eighth century B.C. to La Tène II, have been found in this style. The decoration of Group IV is less regular and consists mainly of incised lines repeated below the lip and above the shoulder of urns, with compound chevrons on the bulge; and a peculiar form (fig. 39 *d*) is oblong in plan with a partition across the middle, probably for ceremonial purposes.

During the Early Iron Age the tribes north-east of the Adriatic were mainly Illyrian, and may have taught the Kelts of central Europe the use of iron. Their bronze vessels were abundant and peculiar, and the harp-shaped brooch they affected

spread to Bohemia and Moravia, Silesia and Posen, but not to the
central or western areas of the Kelts.   South of the Julian Alps
lay Venetia, where the bronze industry was also fully developed
(pp. 31, 92), and the old name of Lake Constance (*Lacus Venetus*)
shows how far the Veneti extended.   Lombardy on the west was
the seat of Ligurians in the neolithic period and of Aryan invaders
in the transition stage (aeneolithic) when lake-dwellings were
in vogue.   The Terramara culture of the lower Po and province of
Emilia is attributed to a Bronze Age invasion from the direction
of Illyria ; and it is thought that kindred invaders were responsible

Fig. 39.—Types of pottery from North Germany.

for the civilization of Bologna (Villanova period) and Etruria before
the Etruscans arrived (ninth century, according to Dr. Randall-
MacIver).

Among the few Italian specimens exhibited in Case 8 the
brooches (*fibulae*) first claim attention, as they help to illustrate the
Hallstatt period, and provide indications of date and cultural
relations before the foundation of Rome in 753 B. C. and during
the Republican period, though this form of dress fastening is
comparatively rare in the purely Roman area.

Reference to the series of early brooches in the Department
of Greek and Roman Antiquities is necessary to illustrate similar
specimens found outside the classical area ; but certain stages in
the evolution of the chief types are here shown.   Prof. Montelius
elaborated a logical scheme for classifying many hundreds of
brooches now preserved in museums but discovered before the days
of scientific excavation.   Seldom are exact particulars of the deposit
or descriptions of associated objects placed on record, and in many

cases even the locality of the discovery is unknown. In spite of these drawbacks, it is possible to determine the relative date of the majority, and an absolute chronology may also be attained in the future. The scheme here presented in outline (fig. 40) will at least assist the memory, though it is by no means suggested that corresponding stages are necessarily contemporary, or that any stage was exclusively represented at any particular period. The simplest and earliest brooch or safety-pin known resembles II a and is named after Peschiera, on Lake Garda, where it was found in pile-dwellings on the shore. It was evidently evolved from the wire-pin, perhaps through the swivel-headed brooch of Scandinavia, and has been dated about 1400 B. C. Whatever its place of origin, the type is extremely ancient, as it has been found in Mycenaean graves on Salamis, near Athens, dating before 1200, in which the type is recognized as intrusive and characteristic of a more primitive dress than the Mycenaean. The evolution of some patterns may have been more rapid than others, and brooches belonging to two or three successive stages may have been worn by the same person. It should be noticed that, except in the compound brooches where the pin and bow are not made in one piece (nos. III d and e of fig. 40), the elasticity is provided by a single or double loop on one side only of the head ; this characteristic, among others, distinguishes them from the La Tène series to be considered later (p. 51). The series I and II began before III and IV, but various forms of II (d and e) proved the most lasting of all, and occur frequently in our own country.

No. I

This series, arranged vertically, starts with a primitive type (a) closely resembling a modern safety-pin, but yet showing an advance on the simplest form named after Peschiera. The bow is plain and becomes stouter and more arched to allow more room for the fabric, while transverse mouldings are added (b), but the main features persist—a single loop at the head and a flat spiral coil beyond the catch. The spiral coil is next flattened out and simplified (c), in a manner recalling the Scandinavian development, shown in the Prehistoric Room, Case H ; and the catch-plate eventually loses all trace of the spiral coil, and offers a surface for engraved ornament (d). The last member of this series shows the disc engraved with characteristic geometric designs, and a last trace of the spiral, but is a by-product in which the catch has been abnormally developed on either side (e). In Greece brooches of any kind are uncommon at this period, but many have a large catch-plate engraved with geometric patterns or animal forms, but vertical (in the same plane as the bow) and generally rectangular.

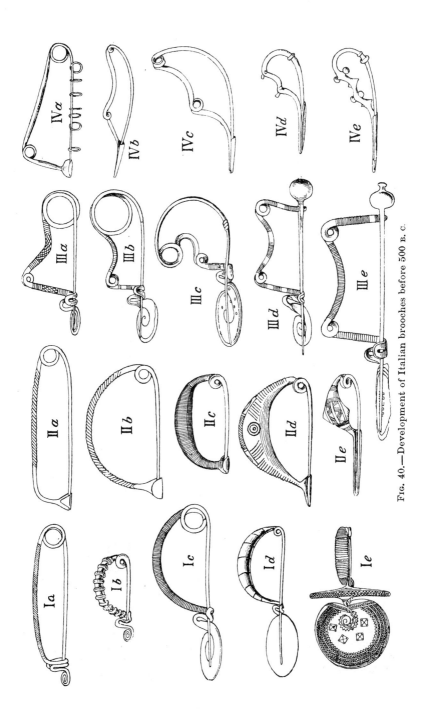

Fig. 40.—Development of Italian brooches before 500 B.C.

No. II

The distinguishing characteristics of this group are a plain bow, a single loop at the head, as in no. I, and a simple broadened catch without a continuing spiral coil (*a*). The bow presently becomes semicircular, and a rope-pattern on it is very usual (*b*); but a thickening towards the centre supervenes, and the ornamentation chiefly consists of transverse grooves (*c*). In the next stage (*d*) the catch-plate lengthens, and the bow assumes the 'leech' form with geometric engraving; while the 'boat' shape emerges on the further lengthening of the catch and hollowing of the bow, the sides of which sometimes run into points (*e*), these being eventually surmounted by knobs (fig. 91).

No. III

The simplest form (*a*) is here marked by a loop near the centre of the bow, but otherwise resembles no. I *a* (plain bow). The spiral coil beyond the catch develops into a flat disc as before, but the pin shows a tendency to curve (*b*), and the loop at the head at length rises vertically over the secondary loop and the catch (*c*). Two by-forms are here included (*d* and *e*) which might be called swivel-brooches, and are made in two pieces, the two loops of the bow being retained and a separate pin revolving on the upper end of the bow. The derivation of the brooch from the pin is here obvious, and a rudimentary form is found in Scandinavia before 1200 B. C. (*Bronze Age Guide*, 2nd ed., p. 133).

No. IV

This series starts with a specimen resembling no. III *a*, but with a simple catch like that in series II. The pin is at first almost straight (*a*), but a curve is soon developed as in the last series, and the next example shows a simultaneous lengthening of the catch (*b*). The curve of the pin and length of the catch increase together (*c*), and the two small loops in the bow are represented by horn-like projections (*d*). The 'horned' type (*e*) is the last here illustrated, some specimens having as many as four pairs of horns or knobbed projections on the bow.

Rich in later developments of the Italian brooch-type is the Giubiasco cemetery in the Ticino valley, from which a series is exhibited. This and similar sites (the earliest dating from the sixth century B. C.) are all near Bellinzona, at the northern end of the Lake Maggiore, and have proved remarkably rich in grave furniture. The pottery and ornaments exhibited in Case 7, together with a similar series in the Department of Greek and Roman Antiquities, are fairly representative of the types discovered; and the brooches have been divided into two main groups. The first of these comprises the following : leech-type, known also as the Golasecca type, named after the cemetery at the southern end of Lake Maggiore : Certosa type (fig. 41), named after the Carthusian monastery (Charterhouse) near Bologna, where the type was commonly found in association with red-figure Greek vases of the sixth and fifth centuries B. C. : the simple bow-brooch with spiral spring (fig. 40, I b), serpentine and horned types (varieties of fig. 40, IV) with heavy catches terminating in knobs (fig. 42).

These are of early patterns distinct from the series of La Tène with bilateral spring, but may nevertheless be late survivals

FIG. 41.—Bronze brooches, Certosa, Bologna. ($\frac{2}{3}$)

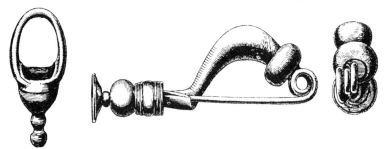

FIG. 42.—Brooch and pendant, Giubiasco, Ticino. ($\frac{2}{3}$)

in a secluded district, and contemporary with those modelled on La Tène I (figs. 43, 44). Authorities are disposed to date the Giubiasco cemetery much later than most of the brooches would indicate elsewhere. A bulky type (fig. 44) inlaid with coral or some similar material has affinities in the Rhone valley and even in England (Arras, Yorks.). This second or Gaulish group includes bronze and iron examples of La Tène I type, as found also in the Marzabotto cemetery (fifth century B. C.), one of several important sites in the vicinity of Bologna ; and certain local types of less importance. A striking feature of these cemeteries is the large number of rings and basket-shaped pendants (fig. 42) attached to the bow of the brooch, especially of the Golasecca type. Amber was worn either on a necklace of spindle-shaped beads or on bronze ear-rings (fig. 45), with a single bead, both the hoop and amber being of exceptional size. Cremation was exceptional on these sites. perhaps occurring only in the Etruscan period

(p. 8), and the majority of the graves were covered with slabs of stone which rested on dry-walling of rectangular plan about 1 ft. high, and generally east-and-west or north-and-south. In spite of this protection, the graves were full of fine sand when opened, and in many cases all traces of the skeleton had disappeared, though the burnt bones were well preserved in the cinerary urns. Most, if not all, of the pottery was made on the wheel, the ware being a reddish-buff, containing a fair proportion of sand and mica. Some of the commonest forms are here illustrated (fig. 46): most of the specimens are plain, but some are ornamented with cordons, and a few specimens were found with lattice design and stripes in black or colour. A sword with chape recalling the trefoil form (fig. 56, no. 1) and curved scabbard-mouth, a knife-sword, and iron helmet

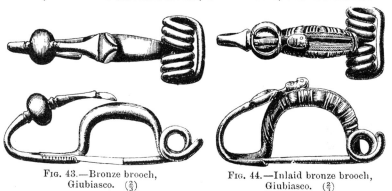

Fig. 43.—Bronze brooch, Giubiasco. $(\frac{2}{3})$

Fig. 44.—Inlaid bronze brooch, Giubiasco. $(\frac{2}{3})$

are published, but very few weapons were found. Beside beaked flagons of the usual Greek pattern (as fig. 53), pottery copies of the succeeding type (fig. 11) were also found. On the whole these cemeteries contain many early forms, with some indications of later occupation ; and it may be that the early culture of La Tène was here developed undisturbed. The St. Gothard pass, which is approached by the upper Ticino valley, seems not to have been used at this period, and the trade-route left the Ticino valley at Bellinzona, to bear eastward up the Moesa to Misox, through the Grisons and so to the head-waters of the Rhine and the chain of Swiss lakes.

Giubiasco is in Switzerland, but on the Italian slope of the Alps, and so distinguishable from Iron Age sites between the lakes of Geneva and Constance. M. Viollier has pointed out that the Swiss plateau has barrows (grave-mounds) with more cremation than inhumation, whereas the surface graves (without mounds) of the valleys contain mostly unburnt bodies. Of the former series the finest example is the Grächwil tomb (north-east of Berne) of

late Hallstatt date ; but only two long iron swords have been found
in the country, and most of the Iron Age burials date between
450 and 50 B.C., when the
Keltic tribes (chiefly the Helvetians) were in possession.

In Switzerland the Hallstatt
period is late, and there may
have been a gap between the
Bronze Age lake-dwellings
(mostly burnt) and the arrival
of iron-using people from the
Danube about 600–550. Cremation and barrows were
characteristic of the Hallstatt
period, and the arrival of Kelts
from south-west Germany involved a double change—the
dead were unburnt, and buried
in cemeteries with no surface indication. In Case 6 are pottery
fragments which, though now
devoid of colour, might have

FIG. 45.—Ear-ring with amber bead,
Giubiasco. (½)

belonged to platters like those in Cases 1, 2 : they come from the
Lac du Bourget in the French Alps, where plentiful remains of
lake-dwellings have been found.

Evidence for the chronology of La Tène I may be found in the
history of Bologna, a town situated at the northern foot of the

FIG. 46.—Types of pottery, Giubiasco. (⅙)

Etruscan Apennines. Before the irruption of the Kelts (Gauls)
about 400 B.C. (p. 3), the site was occupied by the Etruscan city
of Felsina, and the Certosa cemetery just outside contains remains
of these inhabitants, as well as brooches and other articles of
definite types. The Etruscans arrived in north Italy towards the

end of the sixth century, and the Certosa brooch (fig. 41) can be assigned as a rule to the fifth century, as it occurs in the later graves of Felsina; while another type, of the same general form, but differing in detail, is found in the Keltic cemetery evidently belonging to the city of Bononia, which was founded by the victors on the ruins of Felsina and became a Latin colony in 189 B. C. This later type of brooch has a bi-lateral spring, which was in use almost throughout the Keltic area during the La Tène period, only yielding to the hinge in early Imperial times.

The remarkable site which has provided a name for the second half of the Early Iron Age in central and western Europe has been known since 1858 and has yielded an extraordinary number of antiquities. It lies in a small bay at the eastern end of the lake of Neuchâtel, Switzerland, but was not a collection of pile-dwellings like those at other points of the lake-shore. Systematic excavation has proved the existence here of a fortified military post which was abandoned before the emigration of the Helvetians in 58 B. C., and probably lasted from 250 to 100 B. C., though the gold coins point to a later beginning. Apart from a later series on a small civil settlement to the west, the antiquities all belong to the middle period of La Tène (La Tène II); but the term (which means ' the Shallows ') is used to cover the four centuries before our era, which are now divided into three periods (p. XII). It has been noticed that the objects discovered are mostly weapons and harness; and there is a marked absence or scarcity of women's ornaments and things connected with family life, pottery-making, fishing, or agriculture. There was more manufactured wood than pottery, and no forges, anvils, or hammers, the swords and other weapons having been brought in a finished condition and stored on the spot. Its position on what was then a navigable river at the junction of three lakes and on one of the principal routes between the mountains was well chosen; and though there are signs of burning, the station was never pillaged, and was only fully revealed when the water-level was lowered between 1868 and 1881.

The evolution of the sword during the period of La Tène is best illustrated in the Morel collection from France (Cases 9-17); but reproductions of several of the best from various sites in Switzerland are exhibited in Case 6. An interesting example with its sheath from the canton of Berne (fig. 47) was given by Mr. Oscar Raphael in 1915, and bears the maker's mark (a boar), like one of several marks discovered at La Tène itself, and therefore datable. The blade is $24\frac{1}{2}$ in. long and was originally furnished with a ' cocked-hat ' guard corresponding to the curve of the scabbard-mouth. Both edges are sharp and well preserved, the reason probably being that they are of a different quality from the rest of the blade. The scabbard is formed of two sheets of the thinnest iron, the front being given a shagreen appearance by means of a stamp; and having a cross-bar $6\frac{1}{2}$ in. from the point. The chape is little more than a thickening of the binding, with no openings beside the point, and therefore late in La Téne II (about 100 B.C.), like many from the type-station. It will be noticed that the loop for suspension is near the mouth of the scabbard, not half-way down as generally in Britain (pl. IX, no. 9). Two scabbards from La Téne (Case 6) show respectively the shagreen surface and loop on the scabbard, and there are two swords from the same site; also three iron brooches typical of La

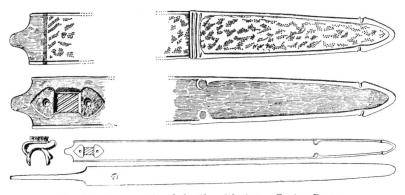

Fig. 47.—Iron sword and sheath, with stamp, Canton Berne.
L. of scabbard, $26\frac{1}{4}$ in.

Tène II (p. 52), an axe-head (fig. 48), a sickle, a spear-head very like that figured from Hallstatt (fig. 32 f), and three others (p. 111), including one of the 'flame' pattern.

Relics from the Helvetian stronghold (*oppidum*) at Tiefenau, Berne, include swords and spear-heads, tapering bars of iron (no doubt ingots, but perhaps used for barter), part of a bridle-bit, and several iron nave-rings from the wheels of chariots. Among other objects found were fragments of chain-mail, horse bones, pottery fragments, and a number of coins from Marseilles and the Keltic area (p. 78). All were buried in confusion, 2 or 3 ft. deep, and bore traces of fire, but the sword-blades were probably not bent intentionally (p. 59). The discovery was made in 1849, and published by Baron de Bonstetten, whose illustrations show brooches of La Téne II type, and swords with curved guards corresponding to the scabbard-mouth, below which are an escutcheon (as fig. 56, no. 1) and engraving as at La Téne itself. It is now thought that Tiefenau was not a battle-field but a station or dépôt like La Tène, with forges and warlike stores, founded perhaps by the Keltic

Helvetians, who attempted to emigrate into Gaul in 58 B. C. but were repulsed by Caesar.

During the early period of La Tène classical influence is still apparent in the sepulchral pottery, and especially in such bronzes as the remarkable flagon with cylindrical spout (fig. 11) found at Waldalgesheim. The form is evidently derived from the classical beaked flagon like that from Somme Bionne (fig. 53) ; and the dotted design (reproduced in line, fig. 11) is not one of the best Keltic adaptations of Greek motives.

The geographical limits for finds of the fifth and fourth centuries include the German mountain-barrier, discoveries having been made both in the Thuringian forest and in Silesia west of the Oder. Eastward they extend to Buda-Pest, with outliers in Transylvania. South of the Alps this type of brooch is fairly common, with corresponding articles, in graves that clearly belonged to the Keltic population of north Italy, and the barbarians have left their mark some way to the south, at least on the east coast, where Sinigaglia (Sena Gallica) perhaps marks the limit of their permanent occupation. Their presence is easily explained from history (p. 3), and the occurrence of Greek or Etruscan wares in their graves shows that they had intimate dealings with their more highly cultured neighbours or subjects. Nor was the borrowing altogether on one side. The Kelts took evident pride in the vases and bronzes, the golden wreaths and toilet articles of Italian civilization, but themselves introduced the long shield

FIG. 48.—Iron socketed celt, La Tène, Switzerland. ($\frac{1}{3}$)

(p. 76) which was retained by the Roman legionary down to the Christian era. They may even have been the bearers of the Hallstatt culture to the West.

The iron sword (Case F) found at La Rochette (Drôme), in the south of France is not known to have been deposited in a grave, but goes to swell the number of weapons showing that the type common at Hallstatt made its way from south Germany and Alsatia to Franche-Comté, Burgundy, and Côte-d'Or, even to Poitou in the west. It measures 32 in. in length, but part of the grip, which originally resembled that of the bronze examples shown with their winged chapes in Case F from Joncquières and Ste Cécile (Vaucluse), is now missing, and the total length was therefore about 35 in. Two other examples of the type are here exhibited (Case 8) from Corbeil (Marne) and Diarville (Meurthe-et-

Moselle), but are not in good condition. The former came from an unburnt burial, and the latter was noticed projecting from the road-surface between Corbeil and Somsois, the handle having been already destroyed by passing vehicles. The original length was about 39 in., and there was a tapering rib on each face, as well as remains of textile rusted to the surface. A burial was subsequently excavated on the same spot, the bones being found in anatomical order and the head at the west end. Two black vases, broken, lay at the feet, and behind the head a bronze razor, of a type commonly found in the Côte-d'Or and neighbouring district.

The collection includes one or two pieces from the extensive cemetery excavated in 1878 at Charvais, in the commune of Heiltz-l'Evêque (Marne). It is specially interesting as showing some of the earliest Iron Age types in this part of France, some of the objects recovered evidently dating from the Hallstatt period, though one brooch, doubtless from a higher level than the rest, must belong to the Gallo-Roman period. Over seventy graves were opened, and all but two or three were orientated with the head at the west end. Among the relics may be mentioned fourteen bronze brooches, usually in pairs, three iron brooches, twelve collars of bronze, some of which are hollow, and three of iron. Coral appeared on a collar and bracelet in the form of unshaped beads, while one ear-ring had large beads of amber on it resembling examples from the Ticino valley (Case 7). There were seventeen bracelets of bronze, of which some were hollow like the collars, others of thin embossed metal, and three iron specimens, while the anklets found were ten in number. Only two vases were recovered entire, but fragments of coarse ware were common in the graves, and one piece of fine black ware was discovered, probably of foreign manufacture. In one grave two solid bronze rings were found on the fore-arm of a skeleton, and the absence of any traces of fastening showed that the bracelets had been worn since childhood, the opening being only $2\frac{1}{4}$ in.

Two or three burials were found in or near a grave-mound at Diarville, Meurthe-et-Moselle, in 1888. In one of them was a skeleton with a torc round the neck, and a wheel-shaped ornament behind the head, having originally belonged perhaps to a leather helmet : the same wheel appears at the side of helmets on certain Gaulish coins and as crests on Gaulish helmets represented on the Roman triumphal arch at Orange (first century A. D.). In the same grave were found two bracelets on the arms, with an oval opening ; and near the right hand a small celt of jadeite, a pair of anklets completing the grave furniture. Further excavations conducted by M. Morel brought to light another grave with a floor of stone slabs : the body, which had been placed with the head at the west end, lay beneath a layer of rough stones. At the feet was a vase of black ware about 3 in. high, decorated at the neck with incised frets ; and inside it was a bronze razor with two loops in a mutilated condition.

The evolution of another series of brooches must here be indicated, though at present it is not at all clear what connexion (if any) there is between the Italic series noticed above (p. 42) and the later group that is named after La Tène. At first sight a link between them seems to be afforded by the Certosa type (fig. 41), but the latter remained practically unchanged during a period that saw several modifications of the La Tène type, and for this among other reasons it is more prudent to omit this Bolognese type from the series now to be investigated, though M. Viollier maintains, on the strength of a find at Multenz, near Bâle, that the Gauls created the La Tène I brooch by doubling the spring of the Certosa type.

The main outlines of development were drawn by Dr. Otto Tischler in 1885, and have not been altered by subsequent investigations, though there are exceptional cases due to the survival of earlier types. In the fifth century B. C. there was in use throughout the upper Rhine area and in certain other parts of central Europe an elaborate and somewhat cumbrous form of brooch ornamented in relief with masks or animal heads, in a style well represented by certain collars in the Morel collection (fig. 59). These specimens were possibly derived from some classical original (perhaps like no. II d of fig. 40), but the prototype is effectively obscured by the extravagant ornamentation : certain of them are compound, that is, with the pin not in one piece with the bow as is the case with La Tène series proper. The treatment of the spring and both ends shows a feeling for symmetry foreign to the Italian series.

In the T-shaped brooch the spiral spring is abnormally extended, and in consequence had to be strengthened and kept in position by a metal axis which in such cases passed through a hole in the head (fig. 36, no. 5). The tension is often increased in the normal pattern by passing the chord (or wire connecting the bilateral coils) under the head of the bow (fig. 49). A single or double coil on either side was, however, found to give sufficient tension in most cases, and the chord is often found on the outside of the spring, away from the head (fig. 50).

The essential similarity between the typical brooch of Dux (north-west frontier of Bohemia) and the Mycenaean pattern, or modern safety-pin, hardly needs pointing out. The pin's point is prevented from slipping out of the catch by the resistance of the coiled wire at the other end, which passes into the bow and is usually thickened in the process. The curved bow, or backbone, of the brooch obviously gives more room than the primitive types (fig. 40, I a, II a) for the folds of cloth pierced by the pin, and the form into which the foot finally passes is the key to its chronology. Brooches of La Tène I type have the foot, which expands for a certain distance to form the catch-plate, turned back towards the bow; but the extremity, which generally has mouldings and faintly resembles a bird's head, barely touches the bow, which is also decorated, generally with transverse mouldings (fig. 49).   It is to this type that most of the Gaulish specimens in the Morel collection belong, and a representative series is arranged on boards in Cases 9, 10.

Certain varieties of this type occur also or exclusively in the following period (La Tène II), for example those with a vase-like terminal on the foot, or a spherical bead of glass in the same

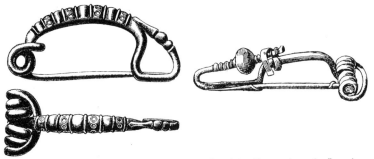

FIG. 49.—Bronze brooch, Dux,   FIG. 50.—Bronze brooch, Jezerine,
Bohemia. ($\frac{1}{1}$)   Bosnia. ($\frac{1}{2}$)

position ; but these exceptions do not invalidate the rule that La Tène I brooches have the foot free of the bow or only just touching it. There was an evident tendency to increase the length of the brooch, and those of the succeeding period (La Tène II), when made of iron, are about twice the size of the preceding. The foot extended in proportion, and was no doubt easily bent in consequence : a contrivance for keeping the end in position is seen on a specimen from Jezerine, Bosnia (fig. 50). This ring or collar became a permanent feature during the middle period of La Tène (fig. 51) and is, indeed, characteristic of the locality which gives its name to the last four centuries B.C. (p. 47). The metal band became an integral part of the bow, and eventually a mere moulding ; but some specimens have the extremity of the foot beaten out and then wrapped round the bow, without any ornamental additions (as fig. 99).

The next stage (La Tène III) is marked by a complete junction of the bow and foot, which now form a continuous curve, with a return to form the catch-plate, and to reach the inner curve of the bow (fig. 52). The open space above the catch-plate is thus roughly triangular, and in course of time is partly filled with crescents (fig. 101), or a step-pattern (fig. 165), eventually becoming a solid

plate (fig. 102). It is at this stage in its evolution that the La
Tène brooch succumbs to the influence of Imperial Rome, and the
by-forms of the early centuries of our era often exhibit a combination of Keltic and Roman patterns.

The above summary indicates the main lines of development, and
will serve as an important aid to chronology : further details and
varieties will be noticed in the description of the Cases (pp. 68, 81,
84, 94). It must always be remembered in applying this test,
that characteristic types were apt to be long-lived, and the date of
a ' find ' (though not of a site) must be governed by the latest type

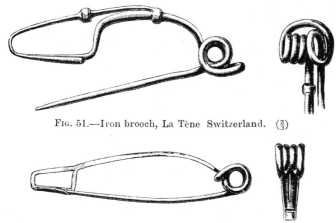

FIG. 51.—Iron brooch, La Tène Switzerland. ($\frac{2}{3}$)

FIG. 52.—Bronze brooch, Swiss lake-dwelling. ($\frac{2}{3}$)

represented. A good example is the station of La Tène itself,
where brooches of La Tène II type are found in conjunction with
La Tène III and even Roman relics ; and a similar succession may
be noticed in the more extensive collection from cemeteries in the
Ticino valley (p. 45).

A few details may now be added as to the affinities of the peoples
who wore these brooches, and shared in the civilization of west-
central Europe during the La Tène period. Caesar, in a well-known
passage, states that in his own day the Belgians, Aquitanians,
and Kelts were distinguished from each other by language, customs
and laws. The Garonne separated the Aquitanians from the
Kelts, while the Marne and Seine separated the latter from the
Belgians. The Aquitanian race is considered by some to survive in
the French Basques, but the two other divisions are more important in the present connexion. The Keltic region extended from
the upper Rhone (north of the Roman province of Narbonensis) to
the Rhine, bordering on the Helvetii of Switzerland and the

E

Sequani of the Jura mountains, while its western limit was the Atlantic.

There seems to have been a fundamental racial distinction between the warlike tribes who sacked Rome or Delphi and the native inhabitants of Caesar's *Gallia Celtica*. This presumed difference has already been noticed (p. 9), but another point deserves attention. The famous Druidical system that Caesar found existing in Gaul, may have been familiar to Aristotle ; and Alexandre Bertrand pointed out that this hierarchy was in Gaul apparently confined to the Keltic area, though its chief seminaries at that time are known from Caesar to have been in Britain. The common people had no voice in the government, and were subject not only to the Druidical caste, but also to the knighthood or nobility who shared the supreme power. This military aristocracy is considered to have been an accretion, due to the ascendancy in Gaul of the fighting stock which scorned amalgamation with the indigenous population of Alpine race.

The Belgae are known to have included twenty-seven tribes in north-east Gaul, most of which were German. Six were undoubtedly of Teutonic blood, while three are marked out as the chief tribes of Belgica and were probably of pure descent. These were the Ambiani, whose capital was at Amiens ; the Atrebates, in the district round Arras ; and the Bellovaci, probably round Breteuil—all near the coast of the Channel, in a line drawn from Calais to Paris. The Belgae were known as the bravest and most warlike people in Gaul, and are represented at the present day in Belgium by the Walloons. While continually fighting among themselves or against the Germans and Kelts, they still coalesced to some extent with their neighbours on the east and south ; and the annual assembly of the tribes in the territory of the Carnutes (vicinity of Chartres) shows that there was in Caesar's time diplomatic communication between the various races.

Of the Belgic tribes the Remi were not the least important, but it must be remembered that though the Gaulish antiquities here exhibited in the Morel collection are almost exclusively from the neighbourhood of their capital (the modern Reims), the burials took place before the arrival of the Remi and belonged to some tribe more purely Keltic. The occurrence of the pedestal urn (figs. 64, 142) in the Marne during La Tène I and in the Belgic area of Britain in La Tène III does not prove its Belgic origin, as a change in the mode of burial during the interval implies some difference of race, and cremation was distinctly a Teutonic rite.

The battle of Sentinum (Umbria) in 295 B c., when the Roman army met the Gauls, is somewhat carefully described by Livy ; and it is clear that the barbarians employed cavalry and chariots on that occasion as well as seventy years later, at the battle of Telamon (Etruria) ; but the Gauls do not seem to have fought

PLATE III. PLAN OF CHARIOT-BURIAL, SOMME BIONNE, MARNE.

[*See* p. 55.

from chariots in Italy after the third century B.C., while this mode of fighting was a novelty to the Romans at Sentinum. In southern France, chariots carrying a warrior and driver were in use among the Gauls about 100 B.C., but we know from Caesar that they had gone out of use before his invasion of the country in 58 B.C. More than a century later they were still used in warfare by certain British tribes. In the Keltic area of the Continent a number of burials have been discovered in which the warrior was buried with his chariot : these form an important class, for the most part richly furnished, and may be approximately dated by the style of ornamentation, and still more precisely by vessels of Greek manufacture sometimes found in association. It is clear that the Kelts were using two-horse chariots in central Europe in the fifth century B.C., and Déchelette has suggested that the long sword was resumed when chariots gave place to cavalry in Gaul.

The richest burial of this kind is that of La Gorge Meillet (Somme Tourbe, Marne), now removed in its entirety to the French national museum at St. Germain. It was strikingly rich in ornaments, and corresponds closely to that of Somme Bionne, containing the harness of two horses, and a bronze flagon (*oenochoè*) of the same Greek type. It had in addition a helmet, of which a cast is exhibited in Case 26 (p. 71), while the sword, lances and spear-head, pottery, and general arrangement of both graves enable us to refer them to the same period and people. A considerable number of chariot-burials have been found in Dépt. Marne (as Prunay, Case G), but several are also known from central Europe, including Switzerland, and a few from Paris and western France.

In the La Gorge Meillet burial coral-mounted ornaments were numerous, and the helmet belonged to a type particularly rare. Two warriors had been interred, one exactly above the other, the heads being at the south end of the grave, and the horse-harness beyond the feet. The Somme Bionne tomb contained only one body, laid between the two wheels of a chariot, the latter standing in two trenches cut below the general level of the grave. Another trench, containing bridle-bits and trappings of two horses, had been cut across the foot of the grave, and was connected by a narrow channel, 30 in. long, in which the pole of the chariot had been placed. The accompanying plate III, reduced from that exhibited in Case 15, from M. Morel's Album, will render a detailed description of the objects and their relative positions unnecessary, while the entire contents of the grave, with the exception of the skeleton, are exhibited in Cases 15 and 16.

The main portion of the grave measured $9\frac{1}{2}$ ft. in length, 6 ft. in breadth, and nearly 4 ft. in depth, while the exterior trench, containing the harness, was about $4\frac{1}{2}$ ft. long, 1 ft. wide, and 14 in. deep. The whole was surrounded by a circular fosse over 3 ft.

wide, with a diameter of about 18 yards, as at Pleurs, Connantre, Marson, and St. Jean-sur-Tourbe (= La Gorge Meillet). Three or four other fosses were noticed in the cemetery of Somme Bionne, but the enclosed burials had been previously rifled.   Graves distinguished in this manner were no doubt those of important personages.

The chariot wheels are 3 ft. in diameter, somewhat larger but narrower than those from Yorkshire (Cases 18, 19). The distance between them was $4\frac{1}{2}$ ft., and it is clear that the lower part of the body rested on the axle and pole of the chariot which were level with the floor of the grave. This implies that the chariot was open in front, though there was no doubt boarding or basket-work at the sides to protect the wheels. Such too must have been the pattern used by the Britons of Caesar's time, for he describes the charioteers as running out on the pole and yoke when travelling at full speed. Illustrations of Greek and Egyptian chariots with the front open are also extant.

FIG. 53.—Bronze flagon, Somme Bionne, Marne. $(\frac{1}{4})$

The open-work bronze plates (plate IV) as well as two moulded discs in Case 69, were evidently attached to the breast-harness of the horses, and other ornaments no doubt belonged to the headstall.   It is satisfactory to be able to date this style of decoration

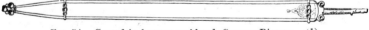

FIG. 54.—Sword in bronze scabbard, Somme Bionne. $(\frac{1}{9})$

(which is also found at La Gorge Meillet) by the vessels of Greek manufacture included in the grave. The flagon (fig. 53) is of a well-known type, for which parallels must be sought in the Department of Greek and Roman Antiquities ; and it should be mentioned that the embossed gold band which was subsequently attached to the front, is probably a diadem which was placed entire in the grave, and was certainly not found in position on the flagon. The kylix belongs to the red-figure period, and may be safely assigned to the fifth century B. C. The third vessel was of Gaulish fabric and much damaged, but resembled in shape and colour the large red-ware urn from Somme Tourbe (Case 17).

On the warrior's left were three iron spits (p. 16) with a knife ; and a plain finger-ring of gold is worthy of special mention as a rarity at that period, another example being found in a grave at Mesnil-les-Hurlus (Case 9). The sword (fig. 54), which was found on the right side of the body (where it was usually worn by the Kelts), forms a convenient starting-point for the series named after La Tène. The development was perhaps not uniform or continuous throughout the Keltic area, but there are certain well-defined stages which seemed to Dr. Tischler to correspond with his type-series of brooches. This evolution can be traced better in the various forms of the scabbard than in the blade of the sword, and a representative series of both is here illustrated (fig. 56, and pl. IX). The Somme Bionne sword has a scabbard $30\frac{3}{4}$ in. long, with a bronze front, which is crossed by two ornamental bands and bears a pounced design near the mouth (fig. 55). The chape is of trefoil form, pierced on either side of the centre, and closely corresponds to two others in the Morel collection (Case 12). One such sword had three coral studs attached to the chape, only two remaining, while in place of the dotted design at the mouth of the scabbard was a bronze escutcheon embossed with three masks (fig. 57). From this trefoil chape of the fifth century was evidently derived the pierced form seen on several swords exhibited from the cemeteries of Marne. The openings became larger and the circular settings passed into slight protuberances, while the outline of the scabbard-mouth, which was simply curved at Somme Bionne, gradually acquired an ogee-curve, that is held to be characteristic of the middle period of La Tène, and is well represented on that site. Swords of this type would therefore agree with the brooches of La Tène II (fig. 51) in the Morel collection, and it is fairly evident that the closed chape (fig. 56, no. 7), is derived from the trefoil through the open series, and is the latest form represented from the Marne district. The ring-chaped sword, of which contemporary examples are shown (fig. 56, no. 5), belongs to a parallel series that seems to be derived from the fish-tailed Hallstatt type (fig. 31, and specimen from Bussy-le-Château) by gradual elongation of the chape, and eventual attachment to the edge of the scabbard. In Case 9 is a short sword in bronze scabbard which may be looked on as one of the earliest stages ; next to it is a dagger in a sheath of bronze with ring-chape (plate IX, no. 8), and the transitional stage may perhaps be detected in the Thames example plate IX, no. 1), in which the terminal has become semicircular, and bears knobs which recur on the typical ring-chape (fig. 119 and fig. 56, no. 6). Early examples, with the simple ring, are known from the chariot-burial of La Gorge Meillet, and the Marson cemetery, both in Dépt. Marne ; while a later date must be given to one found in a burnt burial at Cernon-sur-Coole, in the same department.

Reserving British developments of the scabbard (p. 108), we may point out the similarity between the latest type in the Champagne

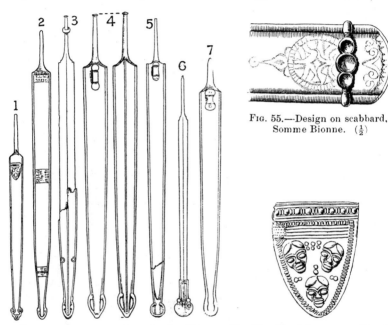

Fig. 55.—Design on scabbard, Somme Bionne. ($\frac{1}{2}$)

Fig. 56.—Iron swords from Gaul. ($\frac{1}{10}$)

Fig. 57.—Escutcheon on scabbard, Marson, Marne. ($\frac{2}{3}$)

series (fig. 56), and the form characteristic of La Tène itself (Case 6). Here recurs the surface-ornamentation below the mouth and the bar with circular depressions as on the Somme Bionne sheath ; but the chape is little more than a thickened binding which, with the aid of circular ears at about one-third of the whole length from the point, keep the back and front of the scabbard together (pl. IX, no. 3). The ogee curve of the mouth is a constant feature of La Tène II. In the upper part of Case 8 may be seen casts of swords found at Alesia (Mont Auxois, Alise-Ste Reine, Côte-d'Or), that can be approximately dated. It was here that in 52 B.C. Vercingetorix made his last stand for Gaulish independence, and the sword-type may be considered characteristic of about 100-50 B. C. The chape had been merged in the binding, and the point of sword and scabbard had been rounded off, while the mouth of the scabbard was now quite straight.

In Flaminius's campaign of 223 B. C. the Insubrian Gauls carried swords only adapted for cutting, which were soon blunted and bent, and had to be straightened on the field with the foot ; but Polybius's statement is now seen to need modification. In La Tène II the Gaulish weapon would have been without the sharp point of La Tène III, and not so long as that type ; but the quality of the metal was excellent (as in Switzerland, p. 48), and the notion that the swords were bent in action may have been due to the discovery in the historian's own day of bent weapons in forgotten Gaulish cemeteries. Three are exhibited in Cases 13, 14 (one from Somsois with a La Tène II brooch), but as the sword was evidently bent in its scabbard, it seems clear that the weapon was purposely rendered useless on its deposition in the grave—either to discourage spoliation, or because the weapon had to be 'killed' in order to accompany its owner. M. Salomon Reinach holds that the property of the dead would be taboo and so unfit for further use.

Something may here be said as to the remarkable short swords with bronze handles of the 'anthropoid' type, exhibited in Cases 8, 19. There can be little doubt that they are derived

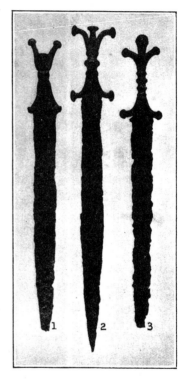

Salon,   Solmona,   Probably
Aube.   Aquila.   Yorkshire.

FIG. 58.—'Anthropoid' short swords. ($\frac{1}{6}$)

from Hallstatt examples with branching terminals (fig. 30). The human head (from which the type is named) in the angle of the pommel grew out of the knob which occurs in that position at Hallstatt, and on what must be the earlier swords of this character, as that from Solmona (fig. 58, no. 2). Of the other two illustrated, one (no. 1) has the human features very clearly marked. It is from a burial discovered in 1873 at Salon (Aube), but the iron sheath in which it was found has perished. The handle is not of solid bronze, but has an iron core, which can be seen at certain points: this method of coating iron is also seen on the Aylesford bucket-handle (p. 126). The face on the other (no. 3) is almost obliterated by use, and the moulding of the grip is a more important element in the decoration. Formerly in the collection of Lord Londesborough, this may well have been found in Yorkshire, and is referred to again (p. 109) in connexion with others from that county, one of which was found with a long sword of ordinary La Tène II type. The Solmona specimen is not the only one found south of the Alps, another being recorded from Malnate (Varese); but most are found in Gaul, and may have been due to the Helvetii of Switzerland. Those with a plain knob (no. 2) are now referred to La Tène II period, while those with heads are shown by fragments from Bibracte and Stradonitz to extend into La Tène III.

The well-known burial at Waldalgesheim (near Bingen on the Rhine) which dates from about 380 B. C., is taken by Dr. Reinecke as typical of his second period (B), which is included in La Tène I. The personal ornaments of this find closely correspond to the bulk of the Morel collection from the Champagne, but the metal pail (fig. 10) shows a departure from the earlier models, and exhibits the drooping palmette which brings it into connexion with Greek art of the period (p. 19). Throughout the Keltic area the grave-mound now becomes less frequent, giving way to large cemeteries containing unburnt burials. There are, however, certain districts in which the grave-mound persisted, and many secondary interments in pre-existing barrows evidently date from this period; but there is not enough evidence to show that these anomalies are due to racial differences or tribal movements. The inclusion of the warrior's chariot and horse-harness in the grave now becomes very exceptional, Waldalgesheim being an isolated case; but we know from history that the fighting-car was still retained by the Kelts, and its presence in the Yorkshire graves seems to show that it persisted in Britain longer than elsewhere.

Ornaments at this stage are more numerous in proportion, and their style shows a certain deterioration. Figure-designs, as opposed to the geometrical, are scarce and badly executed, being sometimes represented by meaningless reliefs or knobs. The brooch of La Tène I type is found in its purest form (fig. 49) at Dux in Bohemia (Case 1), and most of the specimens in the Morel collection are intimately connected with it, though some are doubtless survivals in the succeeding period, as may be the case in Britain (figs. 94–98). They are massed in Cases 9 and 10 to illustrate the three stages of evolution during the period of La Tène; and in the adjoining Cases 8–12 are most of the more decorative torcs or bronze collars of La Tène I in this collection. The ornament is generally in relief and often confined to the two ends. It consists of scroll-work, evidently derived from classical models, but much debased, and sometimes includes masks that recall the earlier style (figs. 59, 60). Armlets and anklets (Cases 13, 14) are generally ornamented in the same way, except that the terminals are wanting and the ring is often complete. Various modes of fastening the torc may be observed in the collection ; for

Fig. 59.—Bronze torc and detail, Dépt. Aube. ($\frac{1}{2}$)

instance, the twisted type, from which the name is derived, has either a rivet (fig, 60, no. 8) or a hook (as at Marson, Courtisols, and Bergères-les-Vertus), though sometimes an unbroken ring (like another from Courtisols) without any fastening. Another method was to break the hoop at one (fig. 60, nos. 2, 5) or two (no. 3) points, a peg and socket junction being rendered possible by the elasticity of the metal. But the most usual form of the torc is an open ring, with enlarged terminals, the latter being worn in front of the neck and giving scope for ornamentation.

The torc as a personal ornament seems to have been derived originally from the East (*Catalogue of Oxus Treasure*, p. 53), and was, like their dress, perhaps borrowed by the Gauls from

Scythian tribes with whom they came in contact along the Danube, then the great commercial highway between the east and west of Europe : the similarity between one with animal-head terminals from Vieille Toulouse (Haute-Garonne), and that on the neck of Darius on the Pompeian mosaic representing the battle of Issus (B. C. 333) should be noticed in this connexion. The collar of twisted metal was a national emblem among the Keltic peoples, and the present name is derived from the Latin *torques*. It is

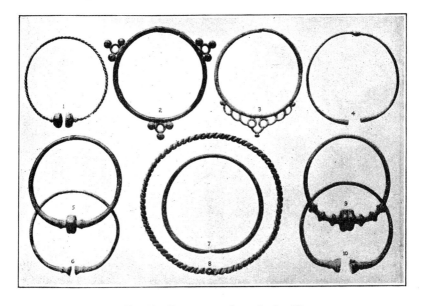

Fig. 60.—Bronze torcs from Gaul.   ($\frac{1}{6}$)

often represented on bronze statuettes (Bronze Room), and on such statues as the 'Dying Gaul' (p. 76). Certainly as early as B.C. 361 this form of collar had reached the West, for in that year Titus Manlius, after slaying a gigantic Gaul, placed the collar of his fallen foe on his own neck and acquired the surname Torquatus. Finds in the graves, however, show that in La Tène I the torc was exclusively worn by women, and it only became part of the male insignia about 300 B.C. Two gold specimens (Case 8) with buffer terminals like fig. 60, nos. 1, 10, are unfortunately without locality. A specimen from Mesnil-les-Hurlus shows that beads and amulets were sometimes strung on the collar, and this fashion may account for the protuberances from the edge of several, either at three points, as from Connantre (fig. 60, no. 2) and Pleurs, or only at the front, as from Fontvanne (no. 3), Pleurs, and the Seine. From articles associated with them in graves, it is evident that tubular collars of plain thin bronze, like those from Marson, Charvais, and Wargemoulin, came quite early in the series : several bracelets of similar construction from the Marne district are included in the collection (Case 13). It should be added that the slight swellings like a plumber's joint (fig. 60, no. 4) seen on examples from Somsois, Étréchy, and Bergères-les-Vertus were no doubt repairs, but possibly became an ornamental feature in some instances. Iron torcs recall the Hallstatt period, when iron was scarce and used for decorative purposes.

Many of the torcs are exhibited with objects found in the same grave ; but those found apart are arranged on boards according to Déchelette's classification. The following are his types : (1) Tubular, sometimes engraved, in some cases containing traces of flexible wood that once served as a core. (2) Plain solid rod, with the ends apart or joined by a catch. (3) Two strands twisted together (the true torc) with some kind of fastening (fig. 60, no. 8). (4) Buffer-type, with the hoop plain or moulded in relief, and ending in a pair of large terminals, generally apart but sometimes joined (fig. 60, nos. 1, 5, 9). (5) Moulded in relief with plain spaces between, opening by means of a movable segment. (6) Ornamented with rosettes and mouldings, often set with coral or enamel, and opening by means of a movable segment or mortise and tenon : abundant in south Germany and Switzerland. (7) Rare type with openwork rings at intervals (fig. 60, no. 2). (8) With triangular or wheel-shaped openwork projecting in front, with movable segment (fig. 60, no. 3). 9. Similar, but with three openwork projections. (10) In form of serpent, only four examples in Alsatia and the Marne (fig. 60, no. 7), of which two are in Case 8.

Apart from the chariot-burial, the cemetery at Somme Bionne contained about eighty graves, more than half of which had been previously rifled. They were in isolated positions, cut in the chalk, and for the most part orientated in the usual way, with the head west. It was observed that several contained bones of the pig, sheep, or other animals that may have been consumed at the funeral feast, and several objects of interest came to light, all presumably of the early Gaulish period except an iron brooch of La Tène II type, $6\frac{1}{2}$ in. long. Beads of amber and coloured glass were worn on ear-rings and bracelets, and one curious amulet consists of two branches of coral (now a pale pink) bound together by a riband of bronze. A pair of typical brooches to be worn on the shoulders retains the connecting chain, which measures $6\frac{1}{2}$ in. ; and the pattern of a pair of open-work bracelets consists of rings separated by triple transverse mouldings. A number of stout bronze rings, like those found with the bridle-bits in the chariot-burial, show considerable skill in casting, and a

gruesome interest attaches to an amulet cut from a human skull
(fig. 61) as at Bergères-les-Vertus. Such relics are common in
southern and north-eastern France, and may be connected with the
practice of trephining skulls which dates back to the Neolithic
period.

The best representative collection in the museum from a cemetery
of La Tène I period is, however, that of Marson, remains from
which may be seen in Cases 9–14 and G. On a site about half a
mile north of the village about 200 Gaulish graves were discovered

FIG. 61.—Skull-
pendant, Somme
Bionne. ($\frac{3}{4}$)

in 1873 on the summit and slope of a hill, some
in groups of four or five, others isolated. The
graves were 5 ft. or less in depth, and several
contained bodies of men, women, and children,
either super-imposed or side by side : in general
they were east and west, the heads at the west end.
Nearly half the trenches had been ransacked,
but in many cases only the western half had been
disturbed, and many vases placed near the feet had
thus been overlooked. Two infants were found
wearing neck-rings of iron, one of them having
been buried in a sitting position at the mother's
head ; and another shared the grave of a man.
One grave contained, at a depth of 14 in., the
body of an infant wearing a twisted collar of bronze ; below, without grave furniture, was the body of a male adult, and at the
bottom of the grave a woman wearing on both fore-arms a bronze
wire bracelet of about 20 coils. On the neck of another skeleton
was a bronze torc, and at the feet an unornamented vase provided
with a cover, 12 in. high.

During the next season's excavations, a warrior was found
buried with his sword, which measured 3 ft. in its scabbard and
had been suspended by four bronze rings ; also, at the feet, three
large urns and a vase that may have been a drinking-cup. The
scabbard has a pierced trefoil at the point, and belongs to the
earliest type (p. 57). A similar terminal may be seen on the sheath
of a short sword (fig. 56, no. 1) measuring nearly 22 in., from the
same cemetery. At the mouth of the scabbard was a bronze
escutcheon (fig. 57) embossed with three human faces ; and four
bronze rings for attachment were also found with this weapon.

Another warrior's grave contained objects of interest. At the
feet were three large vases, two of which had covers, and the third
was of a fine black ware, with angular outline, the shoulder having
an incised fret-pattern, and the neck two bands of bordered chevrons. On the left of the head were three javelin-heads, and along
the right thigh the remains of what had perhaps been a quiver.
Another grave contained a man and a woman, the former with a
curved iron knife and lance, the latter with a bronze necklet and

three brooches of early type placed respectively on each shoulder and behind the head. On each wrist was a bracelet and on the left hand a finger-ring, also of bronze.

Among the feminine ornaments recovered from this cemetery was a pair of white glass bracelets; and from the undisturbed grave of a young girl come three vases of fine ware decorated in red, two oval bronze bracelets, a small brooch from each shoulder, a necklet of the ordinary form, and a pair of hollow gold ear-rings. The pottery vessels mentioned above, with several others of various forms and colours, fill the upper shelves of Cases 11, 12; and from their ornament, as well as from the brooch-types found on the site, it may safely be inferred that the cemetery was closed before the middle period of La Tène commenced. Its richness and uniformity give us a standard by which to judge of the relative dates of the Marne cemeteries here represented.

Two distinct Gaulish burial-grounds have been discovered at Courtisols, a village on the river Vesle, Marne. One known as Les Grands Ayeux was situated near the river, west of the church of St. Memmie, and contained, among many tombs rifled in the past, two undisturbed interments of interest, examined by M. Morel in 1873. In one, the body had been laid with the head at the east end of the grave, having on the left wrist a bronze bracelet, a plain collar of bronze on the neck, and a brooch (La Tène I) on the breast, ornamented with a small bead of glass-paste or coral. At the feet were two pottery vessels, one resembling in shape the bronze sepulchral urns of Etruria, the other like a porringer. The second burial was probably of a woman, and was richly furnished, the orientation being the same as the preceding. A fine bronze torc was on the neck, the fastening being at the back, and below the jaw lay a pair of brooches, of the same pattern as before, connected by a bronze chain, while a third was at the back of the neck. On each wrist was a bronze bracelet, and on the left hand a finger-ring of two coils. Five pottery vessels and a knife were found at the feet, the former containing bones of the pig and sheep. One of the vessels had a graceful form resembling specimens from Somsois and Montfercaut (pl. VI, no. 8), and another was provided with a cover.

A third woman's grave contained a torc without an opening, which had been placed, not on the neck, but as a diadem on the head. A curious bronze étui, like one from Martroys (Aisne), was found with five blue glass beads which had evidently been attached to it, there being five holes for the purpose. A very fine metallic point was found within the bronze socket. Two bracelets and a pair of brooches (La Tène I) were found in position; and a large vase with fragments of two others lay at the feet. About thirty interments were examined in all at different times, but

more than half contained nothing of importance. A strip of
iron, 34 in. long, found beside the skeleton of a man, may be part
of a scabbard, the other face having no doubt been of wood or
leather and fastened by means of the hooks remaining on the
edges of the iron.

Another site at Courtisols, called 'les Closeaux de la Conche'
has yielded about thirty isolated burials, not arranged in any
particular order, and sometimes as much as 50 yards apart, as at
Marson, about 6 miles from the site. More than half these
interments had been already disturbed. but several relics of
archaeological value were obtained by M. Morel. A man of large
stature had been buried with an iron brooch on the left shoulder,
and a pair of iron shears on the right side ; while behind the
head of another were found shears and an iron razor, both of
which had been enclosed in one case of wood or leather. In one
large square grave two skeletons were found, one placed across
the other : with the lower was a sword in its iron scabbard,
a knife beside it, and a black-ware vase at the feet. In the grave
of a woman was a bronze bracelet of large proportions which had
been cast hollow and filled with some white substance : there
were also twelve bronze rings of various sizes, and a catch,
possibly used together as a belt, or to loop up the dress at various
points ; and in another woman's grave here a dozen similar rings
were found, with a catch that could hold several at one time (as
at Pleurs).

This cemetery is remarkable for the fine torcs recovered from
certain graves. One has three triple raised bands on either side
of the large buffer-shaped terminals, and another has ornament in
relief at the terminals and also in front (as worn on the neck),
consisting of the human face and graceful scroll-work. A very
similar example was found in a grave at Avon-Fontenay, in the
adjoining department of Aube, and a third is known from
Aulnizeux, Marne.

To the north of the village of Prosnes, on the right of the
road to Moronvillers, about sixty interments were found in a flat
area at the base of a hill. Several fine urns (Cases 13, 14) were
recovered, and among them were cordoned examples resembling
those of Somme Bionne, the brooches being also of the early
La Tène type. One large vase had lost its moulded neck before
deposit in the grave, but its shoulder bears a remarkable but
rudely executed design between two pairs of incised lines, the
upper pair being irregularly drawn. Two iron spear-heads, two
short swords in scabbards, knives, and personal ornaments are
included, as well as amber-beads and shells pierced for use as
pendants. It should be observed that brooches from this cemetery
closely correspond to the Dux type (fig. 49), which is taken as the
standard for La Tène I period.

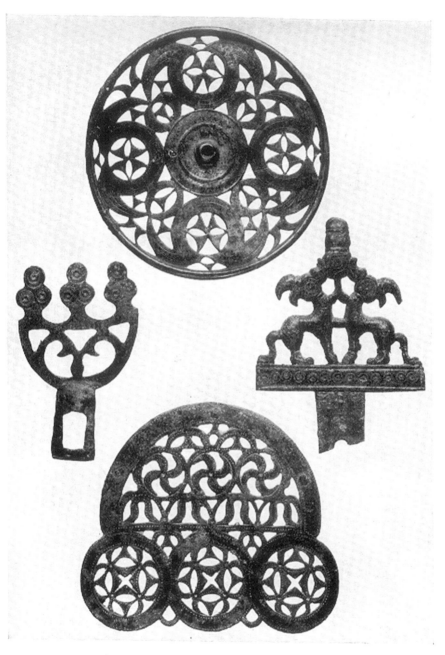

PLATE IV. OPEN-WORK BRONZE ORNAMENTS, SOMME BIONNE, MARNE. (1/1)

[See p. 56.

PLATE V. TYPES OF GAULISH POTTERY (MOREL COLLECTION). ($^1/_6$)

[See p. 70.

PLATE VII. OPEN-WORK BRONZE PLAQUES FROM RUSSIA. (^{2}/$_3$)

[*See* p. 84.

PLATE IX. SCABBARDS FROM ENGLAND AND THE CONTINENT. ($^1/_6$)

[*See* pp. 57, 108.

The greater part of the relics from the Gaulish burials at Bussy-le-Château are preserved in the French Museum of National Antiquities, but no details are recorded of the excavations, which extended over several years. M. Morel acquired a representative series, including a small brooch (La Tène I) with chain, and a ring at the other end instead of a corresponding brooch : also an ear-ring of bronze from the same grave, but resembling in form those of gold from Marson. A hollow ring of bronze, of which several are included in the collection, is thought to have been used to ventilate the helmet of a warrior; while iron rings of somewhat similar shape seem to have belonged to the sword-belt. Iron spear-heads and knives, bronze torcs and ornamented bracelets, besides a number of plain and ornamented vessels of pottery (Case 17), complete the series from this site, except for an iron sword with its scabbard (fig. 56, no. 2), decorated by means of three bronze bands embossed with scrolls of S form ; and two daggers, one with a natural horn handle, the other with a cross-bar pommel and a bronze sheath, the chape of the last being of fish-tail form (as fig. 31).

The first discovery at Pleurs, Marne, was made in 1851, about one mile south-east of the village, but it was not till eighteen years later that excavations on the same spot were conducted by M. Morel. A circular trench was discovered, over a yard wide and 13 yards in diameter, recalling that at Somme Bionne ; and in the centre was a deep fire-place, filled up with black earth and burnt human bones, but it is doubtful if this had served as an *ustrinum* or *bustum* (place for cremating the dead). In addition to the earliest find, which consisted of a remarkable torc and two brooches from a burial, five other interments were met with in the enclosed area. To the east was part of another circular trench with burials at the circumference, and to the west a group of six interments that may have been enclosed. Within the complete trench the area was apparently divided into two parts, one half being assigned to the chief or other distinguished person (with the finest bronze collar), the other being shared by six adults in five graves, three of which were placed symmetrically with reference to the fire-place in the centre of the ring, the feet in these cases being at the east end of the grave. In the double grave near the trench lay a man and woman side by side, the latter without ornament, and the former with a bronze finger-ring on the left hand, an iron brooch on the breast, and a bronze toe-ring on the left foot. Another toe-ring, but of iron, was found in the same cemetery, and in the western group two bronze rings were found in position on the ankles of a skeleton. The absence of weapons was a noticeable feature of this cemetery, though a two-edged sword was found in one of the isolated graves on the way to Angluzelles. Other objects of interest are, however,

illustrated by M. Morel, and include a bronze catch on which
were found several rings of the same metal.   Similar clasps are
known from other cemeteries of Gaul, and it has been supposed,
with some reason, that the rings were attached to the clothing
in a vertical line, and were hooked on to the catch as occasion required, thus giving freedom of movement.   A good example of an
iron brooch (La Tène I), $6\frac{1}{2}$ in. long, occurred here, but special
attention must be drawn to two rare brooches ornamented with
coral attached by bronze rivets to the bow (figs. 62, 63).   These
brooches differ in form but must be approximately contemporary,
though the longer one suggests La Tène III (p. 53).   Both are

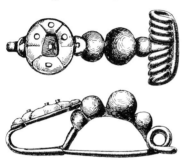

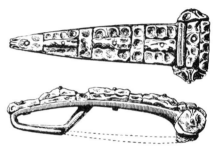

Fig. 62.—Brooch with coral,
Pleurs, Marne.   ($\frac{2}{3}$)

Fig. 63.—Brooch with coral,
Pleurs.   ($\frac{2}{3}$)

of special interest as presenting certain points of resemblance to
specimens from Yorkshire, which have plates of coral attached
by central rivets, and a rosette on the end of the upturned foot.
A bracelet is noticeable for a mode of fastening known in Britain
(fig. 126) and also employed on collars from this cemetery and on
others from north-east France in Cases 11, 12: the loose end is
furnished with a tenon that is kept in a corresponding mortise
by the elasticity of the ring.   The open-work projections on two
collars (fig. 60, no. 3) are not unusual and have been already
referred to (p. 63).

Two sites quite close to one another have been excavated near
Bergères-les-Vertus, Marne.   On the western slope of Cormont,
at a place called Montaignesson, about $2\frac{1}{2}$ miles from Vertus,
a large cemetery was discovered in 1845, and several graves were
found to have contained more than one body, but the bones were
in great disorder and may have been previously disturbed.   On
the other side of the hill, at a spot called Les Croncs (circles),
nearly eighty graves came to light, some of which contained two,
three, and even four burials one above the other.   Altogether
thirty-one torcs were recovered, forty-five urns (some in Case 10),

thirty-five lance-heads of iron, seventy-five bronze bracelets, eleven swords of iron in scabbards of the same metal, with a uniform length of 28½ in., twenty-five brooches and a number of beads of amber, glass, and jade. In one grave had been buried a man and woman face to face, with their wrists united by a bronze ring which had been fastened at the time of burial. The relics that passed into the hands of M. Morel comprise a fine torc, properly so called, with a quatrefoil fastening like one found at Étréchy: two collars that had been repaired somewhat clumsily, and two interesting amulets consisting of a pierced shell and tooth on bronze wire, such as were found in the burial pits of Tours-sur-Marne : also, a disc of human skull, like that noticed from Somme Bionne (fig. 61), with three perforations and marks of the bronze wire attachment.

In 1890 five Gaulish burials were discovered at Mesnil-les-Hurlus, Dépt. Marne, one being of exceptional interest. A woman had been buried with a torc, two bracelets, two brooches, all of bronze, two pottery vases, and a gold ring. The torc is of the usual buffer-type but the ornamentation is uncommon, consisting of S-scrolls in relief (p. 61) : the bracelets are closed, with geometric designs incised on the outside ; and the brooches are of usual types, one having a coral stud set in the returning foot. Of the vases (Case G), one is of 'carinated' form, evidently copied from a metal original and made of fine black paste resembling that of Greek vases : the other is of imposing dimensions, and is decorated above the shoulder with incised frets and two bands of chevrons. The gold finger-ring is quite plain, and belongs to a very small group of ornaments from the Marne cemeteries. Ear-rings of the same metal were found at Marson, and a finger-ring in the chariot-burial at Somme Bionne, while gold on the Wargemoulin brooches has been noticed. Though more than fifty chariot-burials have been brought to light in the department of the Marne, only about thirty-five were found intact, and it is probable that any articles of gold were abstracted by those who were first on the scene, possibly the Frankish invaders.

Among other finds in this cemetery may be mentioned a bronze torc (Case 11) to which are attached as pendants two beads of blue glass, the rounded end (condyle) of an ox-bone, and a piece of iron pyrites ; while a woman's grave contained part of an open-work bronze horse-trapping of the same character as three in the chariot-burial at Somme Bionne (pl. IV).

After this survey of the chief Gaulish cemeteries represented in the Morel collection, a few general remarks on the pottery will not be out of place. The best specimens are arranged in Standard-case G, the rest on shelves in Cases 9–17. Where localities are not stated, it must be understood that the vases probably came from the Marne district, and belong to the early or middle period of La Tène culture. Some pieces may well belong to the fifth century, when classical models were somewhat closely followed, and there will be no difficulty in recognizing the Greek fret in a simplified form painted on the Marson bowl (pl. V, no. 1) and the urn from Mesnil-les-Hurlus (no. 10). Painted decoration, in the form of chevrons, may also be distinguished on a red-ware vase from Marson (no. 9). This is a poor specimen of irregular profile, probably derived from the pear-shaped form with pedestal common at Somme Bionne (no. 13) and in Kent (fig. 142, nos. 1, 4, 5). The pedestal urn constitutes a definite type, and is characterized by cordons or bands in relief above the shoulder and round the foot, the latter being hollow (fig. 64) as in several examples from Essex (p. 129). The type is in reality derived from a tall urn, like no. 12 (Mesnil-les-Hurlus), with angular or carinated shoulder recalling a prototype in metal. Such sharp profiles occur in the Marson series, on vases (no. 7) with incised panels at intervals and bands of sunk lines filled with red pigment. Red lines are also found on drinking cups, as from Mesnil (no. 2), Lacroix (no. 3), and Marson. Vessels decorated in this way are generally of thin well-baked blackware,

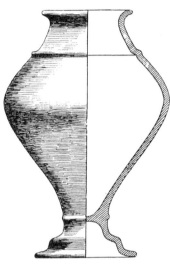

Fig. 64.—Pedestal urn and section, Somme Bionne. ($\frac{1}{4}$)

that seems to be an imitation of contemporary Etruscan *bucchero* ware; but the more usual ware is thicker, with burnished surface, ranging in colour between black and light brown. Somewhat elaborate forms are found, as, for instance, bowls on a more or less developed foot (no. 4, Somsois); but generally the profiles are more convenient for the potter (no. 6, Reims), and wide-mouthed urns, with or without a cover (no. 5, Bergères-les-Vertus), are frequently found in the graves. The decoration is sometimes of the finger-nail order (no. 8, Marson), but more often executed with a point, either by stabbing, or tracing chevrons and other simple patterns. Comb-markings are not uncommon, and a lustrous black line for linear design is secured in several cases by drawing a blunt burnishing point across the clay before firing: a good example is the pear-shaped cinerary urn from

St. Remy-sur-Bussy (no. 11), derived from the pedestal urn but without the hollow foot, and probably among the latest pieces in the Morel collection (p. 76).

A fine pedestal urn (pl. VI, no. 5) with another form of painted decoration is in Case G (Prunay). The ware is reddish, and the body is covered with scrolls in a brown pigment. Adjoining it is a vase (no. 4) from the same department, of buff ware, with red scrolls resembling in form the incised ornamentation of some British specimens (fig. 150). The third painted vessel of this class illustrated is also from Beine (pl. VI, no. 6), with a buff rosette on two sides and a broad red band round the neck and foot.

According to Déchelette, the painted pottery displaying the curved or spiral forms characteristic of La Tène art, is found all over France (except in Armorica and the south-east provinces), on the Rhine, and in the west of Switzerland. It is also known from the isolated Hradischt (*oppidum*) of Stradonitz in Bohemia. This class of ware with painted decoration, like the vases in Case G from Prunay and Beine, must be distinguished from that with incised decoration. They may have developed concurrently, and were derived from a common source, but belong to different areas—the incised examples occurring in Armorica and Great Britain, just where the painted ware is wanting ; but this appears again in La Tène III at Mont Beuvray in Saône-et-Loire (p. 79). The area in which painting is found was then more accessible to the civilization of the south ; and Déchelette suggested that while the decorative medium was no doubt adopted from the Greek and Etruscan wares common in central Europe (as at Somme Bionne) during the fifth and fourth centuries B.C., the patterns and forms of the pottery were independently evolved by the potters of ancient Gaul.

Casts of two Gaulish helmets and a bronze original in Case 26 must be briefly noticed here. They were all found in Dépt. Marne, and those represented by casts are approximately of the same date, which can be fixed, inasmuch as the chariot-burial of La Gorge Meillet, in which one was found, must be contemporary with that of Somme Bionne (p. 55). This specimen has studs of coral set in bronze discs and a broad band of engraved ornament round the lower part. The pattern is a modification of the Greek fret, executed in wavy lines, and is to be met with on some pottery of the period ; while that on the Berru helmet shows the transformation of the palmette in Keltic hands, and should be viewed in connexion with the Waldalgesheim find (p. 20). In the seventh and earlier centuries B.C. such helmets were common in Assyria, and one from Van, Kurdistan, is exhibited in the Babylonian and Assyrian Room ; but it is now thought that helmets of La Tène date were modelled on Greek rather than oriental types.

The bronze helmet from Coolus (fig. 65) is altogether of a different type, and must be referred to a somewhat later date, perhaps the second century B.C. There has been no knob affixed to the top, and in form it roughly resembles a jockey-cap. The projection, which is ornamented with chevrons of punched dots, is more probably a neck-guard (as on Roman specimens from Britain) than a peak, and a very similar helmet is known from Breuvannes (Haute Marne): both are evidently of Gaulish origin.

It has been already pointed out that the bulk of the Morel collection of Gaulish antiquities belongs to the early period

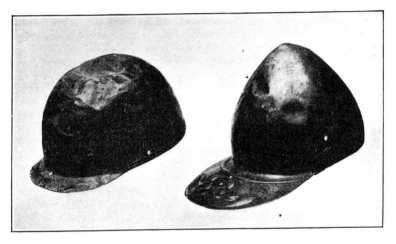

Fig. 65.—Bronze helmets, Coolus (Marne) and England. ($\frac{1}{6}$)

of the La Tène civilization, and special attention should therefore be drawn to the remains from the cemeteries which represent the succeeding period, when the brooch had the end of the returned foot attached to the bow (p. 52). Those in bronze are of the average size, but some examples in iron attain exceptional proportions, one measuring 9 in. in length.

In 1863 a Gaulish cemetery was discovered on the road between Somsois and Champaubert, not half a mile from the former village. The interments had been made on the slope of a hill, close to an ancient road, and extended over an area of about 300 square yards. Above the bodies was a layer of black earth, 8 to 12 in. thick, surmounted by a compact layer of chalk, 2 ft. thick, below the soil. On this site no uniformity was observed in the orientation, the graves being cut in several directions. The bodies had been buried at full length, and lay on the back with the arms by the sides, the legs being crossed in two exceptional cases. It was noticed that in about a third of the total number of graves, one or two sherds of pottery had been intentionally included. In the grave of a warrior was a sword bent at a sharp angle, as well as the chain which served as a sword-belt, also a shield boss of the usual form. The shield itself seems to have been made of wood with metal edging, and apparently had an oblong form. In what was evidently a woman's grave were found two jet rings, one on the right upper-arm, the other on the wrist, while on either ankle was an ornamental ring of bronze. Elsewhere another armlet was found in position on the upper arm, with an opening of $2\frac{3}{4}$ in. Another grave contained the remains of a young girl, with two bronze brooches of La Tène II type lying close to one another on the breast. A fine bowl-shaped vase of black ware was lying between the left arm and body in another grave, which contained also a necklace of blue glass and amber beads, a bronze bracelet on the left wrist, and an iron goblet of which the exact shape could not be determined. The richest grave yielded, in addition to a bracelet on the left wrist, and a pair of anklets, a fine bronze sword-chain or baldric of thirty-six triple links, lying in a heap at the left thigh, some amber beads near the throat, two bronze brooches of La Tène II, and a fine bronze collar on the neck.

At a spot known as Pont de l'Isle, between Corroy and Gourgançon, six burials were found close together, and two warriors placed together in the central grave in opposite directions. On the left arm of a woman was a bronze ring, one of glass on the wrist and two iron brooches on the breast. The massive armlet of jet or shale was from another grave. In this cemetery were also found examples of a very long and ill-balanced iron sword usually associated with the station of La Tène ; one is exhibited in Case 16 (plate IX, no. 5), but no record exists of any objects found in association with it. Some fragments of the iron scabbard still remain on the blade, and the mounts show a close resemblance to a British specimen from the Thames (plate IX, no. 4).

The collection includes two brooches from a cemetery at Wargemoulin (Marne), but it is quite uncertain whether they were taken from the same grave. One is La Tène II, common enough in certain districts of central Europe but rare in Marne, and its occurrence here suggests a comparatively late date for the other brooch, which is of a remarkable character. It is ornamented with pellets of coral in two bands, the inner fixed by bronze pins projecting from the solid central disc, the outer by pins radiating from the edge. The central boss is surmounted by a solitary pellet, and the bronze groundwork is covered with embossed gold foil. Part of a simpler brooch, on the same principle, is exhibited beside it.

On a tongue of high chalky ground at Montfercaut, eight miles east of Châlons-sur-Marne, M. Morel discovered in 1873 the solitary burial of a warrior. The grave was about 4 ft. deep and ran east and west, the head lying at the west end (fig. 66). The trench was filled with chalk, with a thin layer of blackish earth overlying the skeleton, which had not apparently been placed in a coffin. On the right side was an iron sword (Case 16) in a

Fig. 66.—Plan of grave,
Montfercaut, Marson.

sheath of the same material, and between it and the body had been placed a lance, about 4½ ft. long, the iron head being by the right knee and the ferrule beside the skull. The bones were well enough preserved to show the posture of the skeleton, and the skull was recovered intact, proving to be highly brachycephalic. A large wooden buckler had been placed on the warrior's left, the heavy boss resting on the hip bone ; and near the left elbow was an iron knife, by the side of which, lying beneath the umbo, lay a pair of iron shears. The grave contained only one piece of pottery, but perhaps the best example of its kind in the collection (pl. VI, no. 8). It had been placed in the corner of the grave to the right of the feet, and is of fine lustrous black ware, turned on the wheel, with a raised band painted red on the shoulder, above a band of engraved ornament (Case G).

In the commune of Connantre, Marne, a group of interments was discovered, including that of a warrior buried as at Montfercaut, Marson, in panoply. The shield, of which the boss rested on the right upper-arm, seems to have been of oval shape and to have been covered with wood, leather, or wickerwork, with a metal edging where it would rest on the ground. The sword lay beside the right leg, and its chain (characteristic of La Tène II) was attached, but not passed round the waist. Beyond, but parallel to the sword, was a reversed spear (as at Montfercaut), the spiked ferrule being on a level with the shoulder. Two iron brooches of the early type, measuring 6¾ and 2¾ in., had been worn, and three iron clamps, the use of which is not clear, lay near the left foot. The cemetery further yielded a fine bronze collar with three lobes, each consisting of a ring with three balls on its circumference (fig. 60, no. 2), like one

1

2

3

4

5

6

7

8

9

PLATE VI. POTTERY FROM GERMANY (TOP ROW) AND FRANCE. ($^1/_6$)

[*See* pp. 38, 71, 74.

from Pleurs. A sword in poor condition retains traces of a
coarse textile near the handle (Case 9). Vases of various forms
were found, and one of Roman appearance contained the bones
of an infant. Several spindle-whorls of terra-cotta were also
recovered.

The Gaulish antiquities hitherto considered have been confined
to a compact area in the north-east of France, between Paris and
Lorraine, the dead being buried unburnt in cemeteries. To the
south of this area a grave-mound was generally raised ; and in
the French Alps inhumation was still practised in the third
and second centuries B. C. much as in the Marne, though later in
date. From the lower Rhone area come the two bronze swords
(fig. 67) with their winged chapes in Case F (Joncquières and Ste.
Cécile, Dépt. Vaucluse) ; and it is in this region that the bronze

FIG. 67.—Bronze swords with chapes, Dépt. Vaucluse. L. of swords, 31 in.

weapon held its own longest against the long iron sword of Hallstatt. In common with Spain the true Iron Age of southern
France began in Hallstatt II, and cremation was the prevailing
funeral rite, due to large Ligurian and Iberian elements in the
population and the influence of Greece. The short sword with
horseshoe pommel (*antennae*) had a long life in these parts, and a
native coinage based on Greek and Sicilian models began in the
third century. The local pottery, distinct from wares imported
from classical lands, was hand-made in the Hallstatt period, La
Tène ware being made on the wheel. But in southern France and
in Spain the influence of La Tène was not so strong as that of
the Greek colonies on the coast ; and the stages of evolution can
be better dated by red-figure vases and coins of various mints than
by the contemporary products of central Europe.

Cremation areas, therefore, lay both north and south of the
central zone where in Hallstatt and early La Tène times inhumation was dominant in western Europe ; and the eventual change
in that zone was no doubt due to influence from both directions.

Special importance attaches to the burnt burial discovered at

St. Remy-sur-Bussy, Marne (Case G). Another has been found at Vitry-le-François in the same department, but this method of burial was undoubtedly but seldom practised in the middle La Tène period. The cinerary urn (plate V, no. 11) was 11 in. high and was buried in black soil over 3 ft. deep. It is of fine polished black ware, and was sealed with a pottery cover. Within were burnt bones, evidently of a woman, with the fused remains of a glass bracelet and the spiral iron spring of a T-pattern brooch (Case 15).

Another burial after cremation has been discovered in the same district at Cernon-sur-Coole, where a cinerary urn $16\frac{1}{2}$ in. high was placed in a circular cist, with a sword about 29 in. long, iron sword-chain, and lance-head. The sword has already been referred to for its chape (p. 58), but a special feature is the scroll work on the scabbard in the style of the Thielle spear-head (fig. 15), surmounted by a loop and curved scabbard-mouth. The burial may be referred to the close of the middle period of La Tène.

The period La Tène II, which includes most of the Iron Age antiquities found at La Tène itself (p. 47), extends from about the death of Alexander the Great (323 B.C.) to the invasions of the Cimbri and Teutones which were checked or diverted by the exploits of Marius and Catulus in the closing years of the second century B.C. This is the middle La Tène period of Tischler (Reinecke's La Tène C), and intervenes between the periods of classical Greek and of Roman influence, the latter being due to the extension of Italian supremacy north of the Alps. It is itself characterized by certain Hellenistic features, as the result of contact with the Balkan peoples, but graves of the period are scarce and poorly furnished, and the evidence derived from such remains as the Pergamum marbles is to some extent vitiated by the artistic licence of the sculptor. The famous monument set up by King Attalus of Pergamum on the Acropolis of Athens to celebrate his defeat of the Gauls in 240 B.C., gave a free rendering of the dress, arms, and appearance of the Keltic warriors at this time ; and the statue of the ' Dying Gaul ' in the Capitol at Rome belongs to a type that took its rise in these circumstances, though the modern restoration of the statue is misleading. The shield generally represented in such works of art is a long oval or rather an irregular polygon (see statuettes in Bronze Room), having in the centre a transverse band of iron, consisting of a half cylinder to protect the grip, and a wing on either side fastened to the wood or leather of the shield (fig. 68). Though earlier shields no doubt existed in central Europe (figs. 1, 6), none with metal fittings can be traced in Gaul before La Tène II, and it is supposed that warriors of the fifth and fourth centuries carried shields made entirely of wood, leather, or wickerwork if they had any defensive armour at all, but Polybius speaks of the Gaesates going stripped into battle.

Subsequently the sides of the boss and the outline of the wings are rounded (as Connantre, fig. 68), and from top to bottom of later shields there also ran a thin metal brace to give additional strength. This seems to have been continuous with the boss when the latter assumed a pointed oval form like those (fig. 68) from Uzès and St. Étienne-au-Temple (neither in the Museum) (p. 106).

The iron spear-heads were sometimes relatively broad, and at La Tène itself often had sinuous outlines (Case 6): the socket is normally complete (not split), and the conical or pyramidal ferrule is fairly common at this stage (*see* one from Connantre), giving from its position in the grave the length of the spear. The

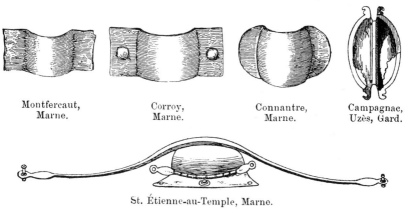

Montfercaut, Corroy, Connantre, Campagnac,
Marne. Marne. Marne. Uzès, Gard.

St. Étienne-au-Temple, Marne.

Fig. 68.—Development of Gaulish shield-bosses. (⅙)

swords are either short as before, with pronounced chapes, or long swords with pointed chapes, while the heavy bronze sword-chain mentioned by Diodorus is often found (as at Somsois and Reims). Chariots and horse-furniture are, on the other hand, rather unexpectedly absent from the graves. Elaborate girdle-chains of peculiar form seem to be confined to this period, and armlets of glass and lignite (or Kimmeridge shale) are included among personal ornaments. Armlets of bronze and iron are also common, consisting of one to two coils, and the knobbed examples of the preceding period are replaced by hollow armlets with nut-shaped lobes, fastened by a hinge. Torcs or collars are barely represented, and the usual buffer type seems to have soon gone completely out of fashion.

The most important class of ornaments has yet to be noticed. The study of types has rendered it almost certain that the early brooches of the Keltic world (La Tène I) passed through various stages before the Roman provincial type, with its many derivatives, was evolved.   The stage known as middle La Tène is marked by the attachment of the returned foot to the bow by means of one or more metal bands or collars which subsequently become merely ornamental features.   It is only natural to class specimens that have the bow and foot distinct but actually fastened by the collar (fig. 50), as nearest the prototype, in which the two parts were not in contact.   Something has been said above as to the history of the brooch during the Early Iron Age, so that it is only necessary here to refer to specimens from La Tène itself (Case 6) and the few included in the Morel collection.

Pottery and metal vessels are almost unknown on sites belonging to this period, but some light is thrown on the relations

between the Keltic and Mediterranean peoples at this time by the coins that now appear in the graves, though they do not become plentiful till the last stage of La Tène civilization.   In some parts the coins are clearly derived from early classical models, those copied from the Philippus (p. 166) being comparatively close to the original, while some struck at Marseilles are more frankly barbarian. In central European unburnt burials of La Tène II and III are sometimes found small gold coins (fig. 69) of rude workmanship called

Fig. 69.—Keltic gold coins, Vetulonia, Etruria.   ($\frac{1}{1}$)

Regenbogenschüsselchen (little rainbow dishes).   These are mostly in Bavaria and Würtemberg, especially in the upper Danube valley, but isolated specimens are known from Switzerland and Bohemia, and even beyond the Thuringian Forest.   The coins are of electrum (gold with silver), and cup-shaped, the German name being probably derived from the superstitious belief that they may be found where the rainbow meets the earth, many having been washed out of the earth by heavy rain.   Another explanation is that the device on a certain number of them was taken for a rainbow, though it is more like the rising sun.

The Keltic area at this period extends eastward, even beyond the Carpathians, but seems to exclude eastern Italy, while North Germany becomes productive.   Large cemeteries were used, and unburnt burials preponderate, though cremation makes its appearance on the Rhine, no doubt in connexion with the southern advance of the Teutons.   There is a strange scarcity of corresponding remains in southern France and the Pyrenees, as well as in south Tyrol and south Switzerland. Upper Italy is in some respects productive, but the important cemeteries in the Ticino Valley exhibit local peculiarities (p. 44).

The foundation of the Roman province of Narbonensis (121 B. C.) in southern Gaul marks the beginning of a new era for the Keltic population ; while extensive operations in Transalpine Gaul four years before showed the determination of Rome to safeguard her frontiers and extend her power. At the same time tribal movements in southern Germany constituted a grave danger to the Republic ; and the Cimbri and Teutones, with other kindred tribes, almost anticipated the conquest of Rome by barbarians five centuries later. The last period (D) of the La Tène civilization corresponds to the closing century of the Roman Republic, and is marked by striking changes, archaic survivals being far outnumbered by complete innovations. Late La Tène antiquities are found, and were no doubt also produced, both in border districts already Romanized and in areas as yet unapproached by Roman arms. Here, then, are the forerunners of Roman provincial art, which had far-reaching effects on the culture of northern Europe : and it is at times difficult to distinguish the Republican and Imperial periods in provincial handiwork.

The typical sword of La Tène III is long and double-edged, not tapering, but with a rounded end not adapted for thrusting. The chape is little more than a thickened binding of the scabbard, the latter being strengthened by several cross-bars of metal at intervals on both faces (plate IX, no. 4) ; but short swords on some sites recall the *gladius* of the legionary. Spear-heads are as a rule, perhaps, larger than before, and the shield-bosses are more oval in form (fig. 68) or have wings of another and less massive kind. Horse-harness is now more plentiful, and remains of two-wheeled chariots have been found, though rarely in graves. A notable feature of this period is the spur, which now first makes its appearance and is no doubt of barbarian origin. The large quantity of tools for agriculture or domestic use is due to the discovery of such prolific sites as the Aeduan capital Bibracte (Mont Beuvray, near Autun), Alise-Sainte Reine (the ancient Alesia) in Côte-d'Or, La Tène itself, the Hradischt (stronghold) of the Boii at Stradonitz (20 miles south-east of Prague), and Gurina (in the upper valley of the Gail, Carinthia). A few specimens of this kind from La Tène are shown in Case 6 (p. 47).

The characteristic brooch of La Tène III derives its alternative name from Nauheim (in the Wetterau, 18 miles north of Frankfurt-on-Main), but survivals of earlier patterns are far from uncommon. Rings for the neck, arm, and finger are not so numerous as before, but armlets are found of iron, hollow bronze, and coloured glass, while on nearly every ornamental object appear the coloured enamels that give a peculiar stamp to La Tène III

(p. 101). On the other hand, toilet articles appear in greater abundance, and include needle-cases (p. 65) mounted with bronze rings of a type already known ; also mirrors which were new to the west of Europe, iron shears, tweezers, and razors.   Coins, too, now become numerous and important, nearly every site yielding a quantity, but very few being found in graves.

The area in which late La Tène finds occur is bounded on the south by upper Italy and Illyria, but the eastern limit is still undefined, while all the Keltic districts of the west have proved productive.   Cremation is now the rule north of the Alps, and burials of this kind are common in North France, but more especially on the Rhine and lower Main.   There is some doubt as to the method adopted in other areas, such as the upper Main and Danube ; but this radical change in funeral customs was evidently due to the Teutonic tribes who migrated southward about this time, and it is significant that north Germany yields remains of this period.   One province seems to include part of Hanover, the Altmark, and Saxony, where a characteristic ceramic type is the black bucket-shaped urn. Another province lies farther to the east, extending to the lower Oder and Vistula ; while the Baltic country is best classed with Scandinavia.

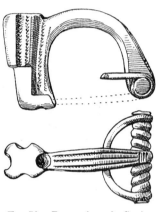

FIG. 70.—Bronze brooch, Spain (side and top views). ($\frac{2}{3}$)

Considerable attention has been given to Spanish archaeology in recent years, and Professor Bosch Gimpera's recent summary of the finds includes cremated burials in the provinces of Barcelona and Gerona with pottery contemporary with the bronze-sword phase of Hallstatt (ninth–seventh centuries) ; and another group in Gerona with pottery like south Gaulish ware, and an iron dagger with horseshoe pommel, assigned to the seventh and sixth centuries.   He divides the local period of La Tène into (1) Post-Hallstatt I, fifth century to about 330 B.C. ; (2) Post-Hallstatt II, from about 330 to 250 B.C. ; (3) Iberian or Keltiberian, represented at Numantia, about 250–133 B.C., when that capital was destroyed by Scipio Africanus the younger.   The Kelts came in the sixth or fifth century B.C. from southern France through the western passes of the Pyrenees, as the Iberians in the northeast of Spain were hardly touched by the Hallstatt culture.   The large iron sword (fig. 29) of Hallstatt is unknown in Spain, but the antennae-sword (like fig. 30) is fairly common; and as this belongs to the period 650–500 in France, it serves to date the Keltic invasion of the Peninsula (p. 4). That a short sword with a point for thrusting was still in use in Spain about 216 B. C. is shown by Livy's account of the battle of Cannae, where Spaniards so armed fought under Hannibal side by side with Gauls, who had long pointless swords, but shields much like the Spanish pattern.

Two forms of the brooch appear to be confined to that country. One is unusually massive and is a later variety of La Tène I, with the foot returned and expanded into a pyramid (fig. 70). The other consists of an expanding bow sometimes approaching the Hallstatt kettledrum form (fig. 71), with a pin attached to

Fig. 71.—Brooch of kettledrum type, Spain. ($\frac{3}{4}$)

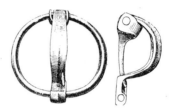

Fig. 72.—Ring-brooch, Despeña Perros, Spain. ($\frac{1}{1}$)

the head by means of a ring which also passes through the foot; and a simple hinge is formed by turning up, on either side of the head, the broadened extremity of the pin (fig. 72). One specimen, of which the fastening is not clearly delineated, was found in association with coins of Greek colonies of the Mediterranean at Denia (on the east coast of Spain in Valencia), where there was a Phocaean colony from Massilia. If the brooch is really contemporary, it must date at least from 400–350 B.C. On the other hand, specimens of the same general form have been found in Spain with purely Roman objects, and the type may have continued till the early Empire. The two specimens here exhibited (Case 5) were found with a large number of the same pattern in the vicinity of what was undoubtedly a shrine, near the pass over the Sierra Morena at Despeña Perros; and their fragile character supports the view that these were votive offerings made for, and offered at, a shrine at this spot by the native miners. The sacred character of the site, which may have been a cave, now filled up with debris, is also indicated by the discovery of several bronze statuettes, of which two examples are shown (fig. 73), and other objects of votive character. The peculiar head-dress of crescent form seen on several of the statuettes occurs also on a British example from the Severn (p. 148), but more evidence is required before much can be deduced from this coincidence.

Iron swords of yataghan type (fig. 74) are another peculiarity of the Early Iron Age of Spain, and the best known site is

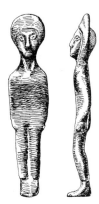

Fig. 73.—Bronze statuette, Despeña Perros. ($\frac{2}{3}$)

Almedinilla, in the south-eastern angle of the province of Cordova, near Priego, where spear-heads with prominent ridges and triangular dagger-blades also occur (Case 5). This type of sword, called *espada falcata* (Greek *kopis* or *machaira*), is of Greek origin and occurs frequently on pottery as a domestic knife, generally on black-figure vases, and as a weapon on red-figure ware, the change both in ceramics and armament taking place towards the end of the sixth century. It was borrowed by peoples in Italy (Picenum and Etruria); and the Greek colonies in Spain (such as Rosas and Ampurias) would account for the appearance of classical models. In a cemetery at Cabrera de Mataró (near Barcelona) a sword of this type was found in such association, and also brooches of La Tène I type with certain variations, while the ring pattern was also represented (as fig. 72).

It was clearly a favourite weapon among the Iberians for centuries, as it is represented on coins of P. Carisius, who was sent as propraetor to Spain, 25 B.C. The Romans had then had a footing in the country for about two centuries, and their presence further

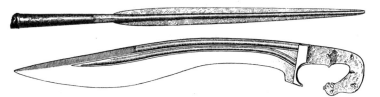

Fig. 74.—Iron sword and spear-head, Almedinilla, Cordova. ($\frac{1}{6}$)

distinguished the Early Iron Age of the Peninsula from that of central and north-western Europe.

In the absence of a purely Roman period, the Early Iron Age of Denmark runs on till the Migration period (fifth century A.D.), and the date of its commencement falls in the fourth century B.C. when La Tène elements reached the Cimbric peninsula (Jutland). This is reflected in the famous peat-bed (moor) finds of Nydam and Thorsbjerg (probably between 400 and 500 A.D.), and the later

Iron Age people inherited this culture, which was brought back to Britain by the Anglo-Saxon invaders. A remarkable find, proving at least trade relations with the south of Europe in the period of La Tène I, is the bronze pail from Möen, which closely resembles fig. 10 (Waldalgesheim, about 380).

Connexions with the Lusatian pottery series have been traced in Troy and Asia Minor, in the Terremare of north Italy, in France (Nièvre, Allier, and even Brittany), and in Holstein, Slesvig, and Jutland. The grooves and cupules on the vase from Skìve, Jutland, illustrate this connexion; and a few other pieces from Denmark are figured (fig. 75) to show the variety of forms in this period. Some bear the fret or (angular) meander pattern

Fig. 75.—Early Iron Age pottery, Denmark.

common in Europe at the time (p. 70); but the ware is soft and uniformly brown, with the design incised, and there is no attempt to produce striking profiles or colour effects.

As will be seen later (p. 88), the Hallstatt culture filtered through to Britain by commercial channels, but southern Scandinavia was at one end of the amber trade-route across Europe and naturally received a larger share of southern metal-work in exchange for the amber of its coasts. Thus the Hallstatt bronze sword is fairly common; and many bronze vessels as well as elements of decoration arrived in the North during the closing centuries of the Bronze Age. The early appearance of the brooch has been already mentioned (p. 41); but no Hallstatt period is recognized, the Bronze Age being followed by the culture of La Tène.

A few specimens from the collection of Mr. James Curle illustrate the diffusion of Early Iron Age types as far north as

Gotland, a Baltic island off the east coast of Sweden.   The small
brooch (fig. 76) with four imitation spirals (originally with central

knobs) is evidently akin to the
type represented by fig. 37, and
is assigned to about 500 B.C.,
being a late Hallstatt form
occurring in the last phase of the
Scandinavian Bronze Age.   A
Gotland variation of an obvious
La Tène brooch is seen in
fig. 77, dating from the second

FIG. 76.—Bronze brooch, Gotland,   FIG. 77.—Bronze brooch, La Tène
        Sweden. ($\frac{1}{1}$)   type, Gotland. ($\frac{3}{4}$)

century B.C. ; and other types before the Christian era are
exhibited on this side of the Gallery, the bulk of the collection
being in Cases 55, 56.   Another local adaptation of a central
European pattern is the swan-necked pin with cupped head (fig. 78),

which shows a parallel development of the
same idea in Scandinavia and Britain
(Case 26).

Of the Russian and Siberian series most
worthy of remark are the open-work bronze
plaques (pl. VII) of Caucasian origin, probably
worn on the belt, though the corner studs
are now only ornamental, and the attachment is by loops and hooks at the back.
The upper plaque represents a deer looking
back and attacked by a hound below, with a
border of S-spirals : the larger has a standing
deer with a hound leaping at its head, a bull
above, and a bird on the ground.   An important detail is the spiral or ring-and-dot
pattern on the fore and hind quarters.
Unframed groups are shown from Siberia :
one a combat between a lioness and eagle,
the other a quadruped with griffon's head
and branching antlers, attacked by a wolf-
like creature.   This remarkable art evidently
flourished in the Asiatic steppes and one
specimen at least found its way to China.

FIG. 78.—Bronze pin,
Gotland (front and
side views). ($\frac{1}{2}$)

According to Dr. Ellis Minns, the resemblance between Siberian and Chinese art may be due to some community of race, to contiguity, or to a common indebtedness to Iranian or some other central Asian art: in each case there seems to have been an intrusion of monsters ultimately derived from Mesopotamia. A

Fig. 79.—Open-work bronze ornaments, S. Russia. (⅖)

jade mount from a Chinese sword scabbard, probably of the Han dynasty (206 B.C.–A.D. 220), found in the Crimea, is of interest in this connexion.

Into this welter of animal motives Greek refinement was introduced from the Black Sea colonies. Under Scythian kings of the 8th-3rd centuries B.C. the traditional methods of the

Fig. 80.—Bronze casting with development, Anán'ino, Vyatka. (⅔)

country were subject to strong classical influence, and the resultant school of art is sometimes called Greco-Scythian; but Prof. Rostovtzeff prefers to call these open-work plaques Sarmato-Caucasian, the Sarmatians having come westward to the steppes of the Kuban in the 3rd–1st centuries B.C. Jewellery almost purely classical from the Crimea is shown (Berthier Delagarde collection) as a basis for local developments in the Later Iron Age (*Anglo-Saxon Guide*, p. 169); and Koban near Vladikavkaz is famous for perhaps the earliest enamels in Europe.

The methods adopted closely resemble those of the La Tène period, the ground being hollowed out to receive the enamel (the *champlevé* process); and the designs consist of running spirals, lozenge diapers, animal forms, and key-patterns, executed on oblong plates to be attached to the girdle.   On the strength of several bronze brooches from this site, belonging to an early Italian

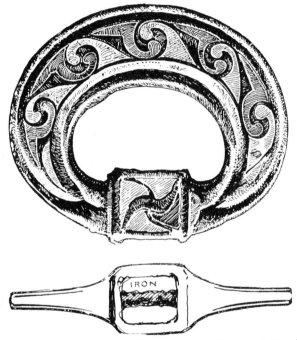

FIG. 81.—Enamelled ' terret,' Fayûm, Egypt, with base view.   ($\frac{1}{1}$)

type (as fig. 40, no. II *b*), Prof. Virchow assigned the cemetery to the tenth and eleventh centuries before our era, but there are indications of a later date, and in so remote a district early forms may well have lingered on for several centuries.   Further exploration in the Caucasus will probably solve one of the greatest current problems of archaeology.

The contents of a grave at Karabak, Erivan, include an iron spear-head, a metal bowl, a triangular plate pierced along the edges, and a large bronze pendant like an inverted five-branched candlestick.   There is an *antennae* dagger of iron from Yeniseisk prov., Siberia, a bronze brooch of La Tène type found near Kiev;

and bronze figurines, model axes, and six small pottery vessels from graves in the Caucasus.

A selection from Baron de Baye's collection has been described by Dr. Ellis Minns. It was amassed during several journeys to Russia and Siberia, 1890–8, and comprises exceptional specimens, which are at present difficult to date. Iron came into S. Russia about 500 B.C. and with it direct influence of the Scythic beast-style. To the next few centuries belong the famous cemetery of Anán'ino (near Elábuga, Govt. Vyatka), and settlements about Perm ; and contemporary with these, but independent, were the Bronze and Early Iron Ages on the upper course of the Yenisei. The prosperity of the Volga and Kama region declined with the Scythian power about 250 B.C. The animal style is seen in fig. 79, and a hollow bronze hemisphere with a hole in the top (fig. 80) encircled by an animal in the act of breaking up, a possible prototype of the so-called Gothic art that spread over Europe in the Migration period (*Anglo-Saxon Guide*, p. 8).

The enamelled terret (fig. 81) from the Fayùm in Case 8 is evidently of British origin, and was perhaps taken to Egypt as a curiosity by some Roman soldier who had served in Britain. Another has recently been found in the south of France at Eauze, Dépt. Gers, and is evidently of the same date and origin.

ANCIENT BRITAIN

Traces of the transition from bronze to iron are not numerous in this country, but the collection includes two iron socketed celts from Walthamstow (fig. 82), and north Wales (with part of its wooden handle), which show the bronze pattern in a new material ; another is known from Lough Mourne, Belfast. Two cinerary urns of a common Bronze Age type (as at Ashford, *Bronze Age Guide*, fig. 64) have been found at Colchester, one containing, besides the ashes of the dead, an iron socketed spear-head with lozenge-shaped blade, and a ring between the blade and socket in the same position as the slight moulding seen on some in this collection (fig. 121, no. 7) ; and the find at Hagbourne Hill in 1803 shows that Bronze Age types were still in use after the introduction of iron in Berkshire. This hoard (Case 26) included two socketed celts of bronze, looped lance-heads, bridle-bits, and pins (one like fig. 105) of the

FIG. 82.—Iron socketed celt, Walthamstow, Essex. (⅓)

same metal ; but also three harness-rings as at Arras, with iron
cross-bars as in the 'terrets' of the period (fig. 81). These were
all found together in a circular excavation 18 in. in diameter at
the bottom of one of several oblong pits about 7 ft. long and
3 ft. wide, which were noticed about 4 ft. from the surface.

It would have been of more importance if described with
greater accuracy, but if the account is to be trusted, there were
found with these objects large bronze rings (probably torcs) and
a number of coins, of which one was silver and another gold.
The pieces were dispersed before details could be obtained (except
that the gold specimen 'was rather large and flat, and perhaps
belonged to the Lower Empire'), and nothing has since been

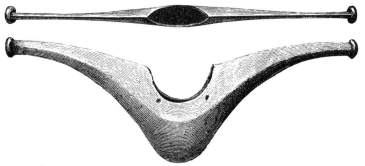

Fig. 83.—Chape of sword-scabbard, Thames. ($\frac{1}{2}$)

published from the site except a socketed celt of the same
description, which so far confirms the evidence afforded by the
deposit here exhibited. The celt found in 1803, though illustrated
at the time, was not included in the find as acquired for the
Museum, but there is no doubt of the second discovery.

The bronze sword of Hallstatt type (fig. 67) is fully represented
in this country and had many predecessors in our Bronze Age ;
while the two winged chapes in the collection (fig. 83) may be
compared with those from the south of France in Case F. The
short iron sword from the Thames (fig. 84) with horse-shoe
pommel (*antennae* type) is generally allowed to be of late Hallstatt
date ; and reference has already been made (p. 25) to several recent
discoveries of pottery that go far to establish a Hallstatt period
in England, as it is less portable than bronze and therefore better
evidence of occupation, especially as the Eastbourne urns were
obviously fired on the spot.

The most striking pieces found, restored, and presented by
Mr. Garnet Wolseley are exhibited in Case 20, and confirm the

Rev. Walter Budgen's discovery at Eastbourne. The site on Park
Brow near Cissbury in the same county was occupied by people
who had little metal but plenty of pottery, the larger and coarser
vessels being of the same order as some from All Cannings Cross ;
and the finer pieces, though devoid of ornament, being of Hallstatt
facies. The bowl with cover (fig. 85) is the most remarkable
and is more difficult to match than the pieces with tall straight

Fig. 84.—Sword of Hallstatt type, Thames. ($\frac{1}{6}$)

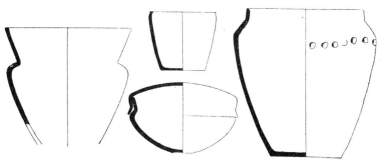

Fig. 85.—Pottery from Park Brow, Cissbury, Sussex. ($\frac{1}{9}$)

neck set at right angles to the shoulder and boldly everted as in
the Salem-Koberstadt series of Germany (seventh century). Other
indications of date will no doubt be found, but this and other
finds contrast both with the rude cinerary urns of the Bronze Age
and the smooth 'soapy' black or brown ware of La Tène type
in Britain.

Fragments from All Cannings Cross (the bulk being at Devizes)
are in an exhibition drawer below Case C on the opposite side
of the gallery. The original shape may be seen in Mrs. Cunnington's book, and this large series is assigned to the fifth and fourth
centuries B.C. mainly on the strength of a La Tène I brooch.
A few diagrams are given (fig. 86) to compare with those found at
Hengistbury, Hants (fig. 87), in 1911–12 by Mr. Bushe-Fox, who
traces the types to Brittany and the Pyrenees ; but at present

most of the Early Iron Age pottery in this country suggests some connexion with various parts of Germany, though finds on the Kent coast, as might be expected, reveal a close similarity to north Gaulish products. Quite different in origin is the black two-handled cup (fig. 88) which is said to have been found in gravel on the bank of the Thames at Barn Elms between Putney and Hammersmith. It is like a Greek *scyphus*, with two horn-

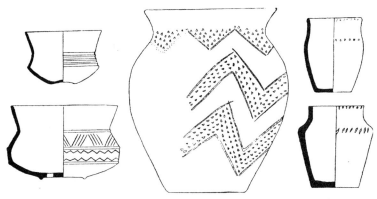

*Fig. 86.—Pottery from All Cannings Cross, Wilts. (nearly ⅙)

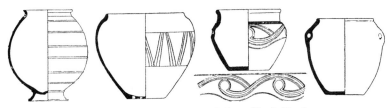

*Fig. 87.—Pottery from Hengistbury Head, Hants.

like projections from the shoulder between the handles; and belongs to the large class of pottery called in German *Buckelkeramik*, but its peculiarities mark it as coming from the neighbourhood of Troy, and its date would be between 1000 and 700 B.C. The small 'kick' or circular indentation in the base is characteristic of certain Hallstatt forms (Cases 1-4), but the horned or bossed pottery of Germany is of different quality, and the handles are decisive, though something similar is found in Italy. If the Thames specimen came here in the ninth century B.C. it lends colour to the theory that Phrygians traded with Britain before the Phoenicians took command of the sea (p. 5).

Unimpeachable evidence of relations with north Italy is afforded by the cordoned bronze bucket (fig. 89) found at Brook-

FIG. 88.—Pottery cup from the Thames. ($\frac{2}{3}$)

FIG. 89.—Cordoned bucket, Weybridge, Surrey. (H. 7 in.)

lands, Weybridge, and given by Mr. William Dale, F.S.A., in 1907. It belongs to a series found in various parts of Italy,

central and western Europe, and dating from the seventh or
sixth century, B. C., the place of manufacture being in the Venetian
area of north Italy. The present specimen is in perfect condition,
with two arched and movable handles, the corrugated body formed

of wrought sheet-bronze bent
round and fastened with rivets,
and the base made separate,
with a broad band in relief and
indented concentric rings at
the centre. The type has been
already mentioned in con-
nexion with Hallstatt (p. 31),
and its occurrence in gravel
under 12 ft. of sand and clay
in Surrey inspires confidence
in dealing with some con-
temporary brooches said to
have been found in our soil.

Another bronze of Italian
origin is the jug from Tewkesbury (fig. 90) with the handle
unattached below as if intended to serve as a hook as
well as a loop. Another very
like it is published from
Bath, and both may be attri-

FIG. 90.—Italian bronze jug,
Tewkesbury. ($\frac{1}{3}$)

buted to the fourth century B. C., that being in all probability the
date also of their importation. Both sites are in the neighbourhood of the most luxurious Roman villas in Britain, and it is

FIG. 91.—Italian brooch, Lakenheath, Suffolk. ($\frac{2}{3}$)

conceivable that their owners were responsible for Italian brooches
and other bronzes found locally.

Contact with the civilization of Italy in the Hallstatt period is
indicated by several brooches in Case 26, of which two are
illustrated. One from the north-west angle of Suffolk (fig. 91) has
lost its pin and can be assigned to the fifth century on account of
its reduced boat-shaped bow with knobs, its long catch-plate and

moulded finial; but that from Box (5 miles north-east of Bath) is a typical boat-shaped brooch of the sixth and seventh century (fig. 92), the sunk decoration on the bow being in the style of the Hallstatt platters (pl. II).

The camp on Hod Hill is clearly of La Tène date, but the brooch illustrated (fig. 93) is a degenerate example of the Italian leech-type (fig. 40, II c); and one practically identical is said to have been found in Cumberland. The three here illustrated have exact counterparts from Italy in Case 8.

No less than seven other museums in the British Isles possess Italian specimens that were presumably found in our soil, and some have been published, including a few from Ireland and Scotland. It must, however, be confessed that the evidence is in most cases very inadequate, and the best authenticated specimens come from the Thames, Hants, and Suffolk; their occurrence in the north of England, Scotland, and Ireland cannot in any case be regarded as evidence that those parts were in direct contact with Italy in the Hallstatt period.

An outline of the development of the brooch named after La Tène has been already given (p. 51), and it is only necessary

FIG. 92.—Italian boat-shaped brooch, Box, Wilts. (½)

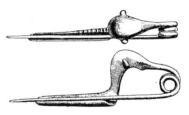

FIG. 93.—Italian brooch, Hod Hill, Dorset. (⅔)

to show here to what extent the series is represented in Britain. About fifty specimens of La Tène I are recorded, and their distribution suggests that they came in course of trade up the Thames and by way of Southampton Water or Hengistbury to Wiltshire and neighbouring counties. A representative series is shown in Case 26, and though the exact place of finding is not always known, there can be no doubt that the type took root

FIG. 94.—Bronze brooch, Box, Wilts.
(top and side views). ($\frac{2}{3}$)

FIG 95 —Bronze brooch, Water Eaton,
Oxon. ($\frac{1}{1}$)

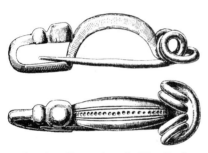

FIG. 96.—Bronze brooch, Blandford,
Dorset. ($\frac{1}{1}$)

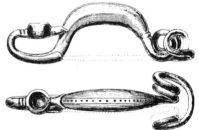

FIG. 97.—Bronze brooch, Avebury,
Wilts. ($\frac{1}{1}$)

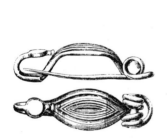

FIG. 98.—Bronze brooch, Thames
at London. ($\frac{1}{1}$)

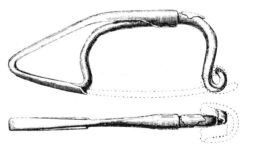

FIG. 99.—Bronze brooch, Royal Exchange,
London. ($\frac{1}{1}$)

in this country not long after it became common in certain parts
of Gaul.

Of La Tène I type another from Box is now published for the
first time (fig. 94); but that from Cowlam (fig. 127) is already

well known and is the more interesting as coming from an interment (p. 116). The pin is missing and the spring damaged, but it is easy to complete the outline by reference to fig. 95. This specimen is engraved with running scrolls (as on fig. 120) and the ring-and-dot pattern, and closely resembles the earliest found at Hunsbury (p. 138). The well-preserved brooch from Dorset (fig. 96) is somewhat earlier than one from the adjoining county (fig. 97), the bow of the latter being slightly clasped by the foot which has lost a setting, probably of coral. One illustrated from

Fig. 100.—Bronze brooch, Walmer, Kent. ($\frac{2}{3}$)

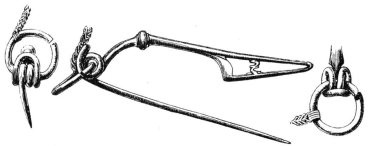

*Fig. 101.—Silver brooch, Great Chesterford, Essex. ($\frac{2}{3}$)

the Thames has the spring supported by an axis of bronze (fig. 98).

Compared with the earlier type, examples of La Tène II in this country are extremely scarce, and that illustrated (fig. 99) is without its spring and pin, but the origin of the collar in the centre of the bow is here demonstrated. One from Spettisbury has a long spiral spring on an iron axis but in one piece with the bow, and has the collar well defined. The fine specimen from Walmer (fig. 100) belongs to the close of this period, the collar becoming merely ornamental and the foot coalescing with the lower part of the bow. The next (fig. 101) is of silver, from a cremation in Essex (p. 122), and is one of a pair connected by a chain, like that from Folkestone, which is almost identical. This is a step in advance and belongs to La Tène III, the open foot being crossed by a pair of crescents, but the general form remaining as before.

The foot soon becomes a solid plate, and several examples of what must have been for some centuries the brooch of the common people are exhibited ; but certain by-forms must now be noticed. The Aylesford pair of brooches had a hook below the collar (fig. 138) and the head spread over the spring like the bell of a trumpet. This idea proved fruitful in Britain, and there will be little difficulty in seeing the origin of such elaborate forms as fig. 102. The ring at the head (as fig. 101) has now become an integral part of the brooch, and the solid foot gives scope for characteristic ornament. The hook on the Aylesford pair occurs also on a similar specimen from Stradonitz, Bohemia ; and double hooks

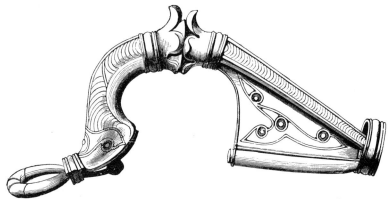

Fig. 102.—Silver-gilt brooch, Backworth, Northumberland. (⅟)

are common on brooches of the period in Pannonia. These no doubt suggested the moulding on the Backworth and later Aesica brooches, but the box-foot seems to be a purely British invention, best exemplified in Northumbria. Instead of the La Tène bilateral coils, the spring now consists of a wire spirally wound on an axis which passes through a loop in the head. The same principle was adopted on another type that dates in Britain from the first and second centuries of our era : an imperfect example (fig. 165) was included in the Polden Hill hoard, and a fine specimen of golden colour was found with other British objects in the bed of the Churn at Cricklade. This type, which preserves the open-work patterns at the foot, is, however, more closely connected with Roman civilization, and has a semi-cylindrical cover to the spring which forms a cross-bar at the head. An intermediate form, in which the tension of the spring is increased by attaching the chord (p. 51) to a hook in the head, is represented in Case 26 (Thames at Hammersmith).

A parallel development can be traced in ornaments of another class — bronze pins for the hair or dress, with a kink in the stem to prevent them falling out in use. At the head of the series stands the swan's-neck pin, of which there seems to have been a peculiar development in Britain and Ireland. It is a common Hallstatt type in parts of Germany and Denmark, and a variety from the Baltic island of Gotland has been already mentioned (p. 84). One (fig. 103) has been found at Woodendean, Sussex (Brighton Museum), and a slight modification is seen in the Hammersmith specimen (fig. 104 *a*), an enlargement of the ring-head producing

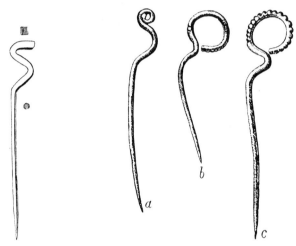

Fig. 103.—Swan's-neck pin, near Brighton. $(\frac{2}{3})$

Fig. 104.—Pins from Thames at Hammersmith. $(\frac{2}{3})$

other varieties (*b*, *c*) from the same site, probably in early La Tène times. Hagbourne Hill yielded, with other interesting pieces in Case 26, a solid casting of this pattern (fig. 105); and decorated examples, with the gradual growth of a stud on the elbow, come from Ireland (Case 25, figs. 106, 107), and may be dated second century B.C. A side issue is the coral-mounted pin from Hammersmith (fig. 108) with exaggerated features; but the simple form of wire undergoes a change in the first century B.C., and has the ring-head in another plane like a tie-pin (fig. 109), heavier castings dating a little later (fig. 110). Pellets and transverse ribbing serve in some cases as ornament (fig. 111), and to these are due the ibex-head type (fig. 112), perhaps early Roman, which in its turn starts the true 'hand-pin', the history of which is summarized in the *Anglo-Saxon Guide*, p. 130. This series of native developments extended apparently over fifteen centuries; and though most of the stages are common to both countries, evolution in Ireland seems to have proceeded on two parallel lines ; and the 'latchet', which the shouldered pin became at an early stage, is unknown in Britain.

Something may here be said of the decorative motives and processes of the early Britains by way of introduction to the study of individual exhibits. An endeavour has been made above to trace their system of eccentric curves to a classical source (p. 19) and the objects illustrated in the following pages will convey some

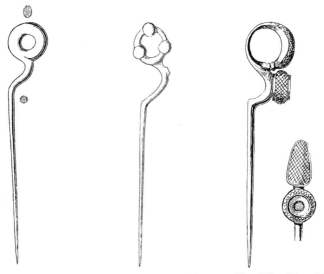

FIG. 105.—Cast bronze pin, Hagbourne Hill, Berks. (⅔)

FIG. 106.—Pin with pellets, Ireland. (⅔)

FIG. 107.—Pin with decorated head, Clough, co. Antrim. (⅔)

idea of the beauty and variety of such designs, as they were gradually developed in our islands.

The *triskele* or three-limbed figure frequently occurs in early British art (as figs. 102, 175), as well as on Keltic coins of Bavaria (p. 78), and seems to be closely related to the swastika or fylfot which was widely known in the ancient world. The peculiar projections on certain classes of bronze-work (figs. 124, 151, 152) are somewhat suggestive of a pair of pouting lips, and are confined to Early British art. This lip-pattern, as it may be called, seems to be originally derived from the Hallstatt civilization, and three typical bracelets from that site (fig. 33) may well account for the nut-design on Gaulish and British bracelets (fig. 128), no. 2 being typologically earlier than nos. 1 and 3. The harness-rings from

Hagbourne Hill and Arras have a similar design, but the British development may have been influenced by embossed bronze-work, the expanding ends of trumpet-curves in relief (fig. 193) being somewhat like the lip-pattern, especially when two such curves are placed end to end. A bronze 'terret' from Leicester (Case 29) shows to what lengths this transformation went in Keltic hands.

Bronzes of the period often have the ground covered with groups of engraved lines in different directions, in a manner suggesting

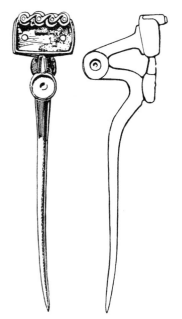
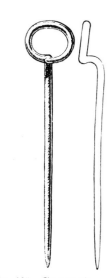

Fig. 108.—Pin with coral, Thames at Hammersmith. ($\frac{2}{3}$)

Fig. 109.—Bronze pin, probably Anglesey. ($\frac{2}{3}$)

basket-work. The Britons are known to have been adepts in the latter industry, and the pattern may, for want of a better term, be so named. It is possible that the hatched triangles seen on classical work (fig. 24) and even on local bronzes (fig. 120) may have suggested this manner of filling the background, but the first appearance of the regular basket-pattern cannot at present be precisely dated. It is well seen on mirrors (fig. 132), and occurs on gold (fig. 175) as well as bronze (fig. 124); while an earlier stage seems to be marked by the engraving on the Grimthorpe shield-boss, and portions of harness from Ashdown, Berks., and Polden Hill.

The golden colour of bronze under certain conditions may have given the impression of gilding, but this process has not yet been proved in Britain prior to the Christian era. The brooches found on the North Wall at Aesica (Great Chesters) are good examples, and date from about A.D. 200–50, while the Backworth brooch (fig. 102) and Upchurch torc (p. 149) may also be mentioned. Gilded bronze was included in the finds at Tre'r Ceiri, Carnarvonshire, and

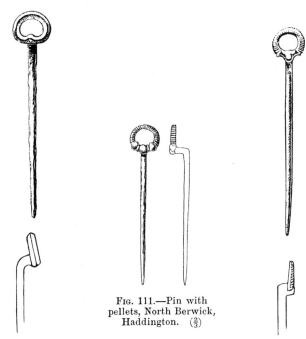

FIG. 111.—Pin with pellets, North Berwick, Haddington. ($\frac{2}{3}$)

FIG. 110.—Cast bronze pin, Ness, Caithness. ($\frac{2}{3}$)

FIG. 112.—Ibex-headed pin, Sandy, Beds. ($\frac{2}{3}$)

at Birdlip, Gloucs. (p. 121), while leather so treated is said to be common in the Early Iron Age of Denmark.

Continental traffic during the Early Iron Age is shown not only by the discovery of several manufactured articles evidently made abroad, but by the use of imported raw materials. Coral is found in south German grave-mounds dating from the close of the Hallstatt period, and was common from France to Hungary, and rare in north Germany, in the early part of the succeeding period of La Tène. Certain discoveries of the kind are said to have been made in south Russia and the Caucasus, but there, as in England, it is difficult to say positively, even after chemical analysis, that the material employed was actually coral.   M. Salomon Reinach has prepared a list of known examples, and contends that the use of coral ceased in Europe between 300 and 250 B.C., its place being taken by enamels coloured in imitation and attached to bronze or other metal in a similar manner. He includes in his list the famous Witham shield (fig. 113) on which the coral is un-mistakable and in excellent condition, but that material seems to have continued in use among the Britons, and an instance has come to light at Colchester, in a La Tène III burial containing cordoned urns with covers. A well-made bronze bowl or cup had a moulded handle, on an angle of which was fixed, by means of a rivet, a stud of this material in good condition. Of several inlaid ornaments found in Yorkshire it is difficult to speak with any certainty, but the two undoubted instances quoted are not exceptional in Britain.

Leaving Koban out of the question, we may trace the use of enamel for the decoration of metal back to La Tène II, in central and western Europe. For purposes of chronology, perhaps the most important discoveries are those at Fla-vigny (Marne), and La Bouvan-dau (Somme Tourbe, Marne), where objects decorated both with coral and enamel have been found associated in cha-riot-burials. According to Dr. Tischler, lumps of red enamel

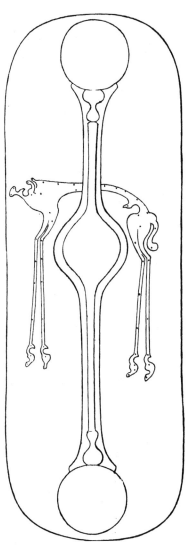

FIG. 113.—Outline of shield, River Witham, Lincs.   ($\frac{1}{8}$)

were at first cut or moulded into domed discs, which were attached by pins through the centre, like the coral they replaced. This method is well exemplified by the ornamental discs found with the Bugthorpe sword (fig. 125); and the Thames shield (plate I) shows another method of applying the bosses to the metal, by light decorative framework.

Up to a certain point enamelling seems to have been developed on parallel lines in this country and abroad, except that enamels on iron, as well as bronze, are common on the Continent. Red was the only colour employed at first, and true enamelling began with the application of a vitreous substance to a metal ground by fusing the powder. The ground was prepared at first by grooving the surface in parallel or crossed lines to key the enamel; and this cross-hatching method may be seen on British helmets (figs. 65, 116) or on the bow of the Walmer brooch (fig. 100). It is probable that this deep scoring of the surface became, in course of centuries, an ornamental feature in itself, apart from the enamelling.

As the craftsman became more skilful, he succeeded in covering larger surfaces with enamel and evolved the *champlevé* process, in which the ground is scooped out to form a bed for the fused material. Nowhere was greater success attained by this method in the Early Iron Age than in Britain; indeed, finds of this description are so rare abroad (fig. 81), that there are solid reasons for supposing this particular style to have been confined to this country, Britain agreeing best with the statement of Philostratus, a Greek sophist at the court of Julia Domna, wife of the emperor Severus. Writing early in the third century of our era, he notices a boar-hunt in describing a series of paintings; and after mentioning the variegated trappings of the horses, adds: 'They say that the barbarians who live in Ocean (the river supposed by the ancients to surround the earth) pour these colours on heated bronze, and that they adhere, become as hard as stone, and preserve the designs that are made in them.'

One or more pieces of red glass paste, of which a specimen is exhibited, have been found in or near the Hill of Tara, co. Meath, and seem to have been unearthed during excavations there about 1860, but overlooked at the time and left on the ground. Another piece, about the size of a man's head, may have come from Kilmessan in the same county, nearly three miles distant, having been discovered in a sand-hill which was removed when the Meath railway was constructed. The incrusted and decomposed condition of the surface showed that the mass had been buried a considerable time, and there can be little doubt that it was connected with the process of enamelling, practised with such success in these islands. The red material, to which the colour of the whole is due, is red oxide of copper (cuprous oxide), and the glass is a tolerably pure silicate of lead and sodium, i. e. a variety of flint glass. The mean

PLATE VIII. EARLY BRITISH ENAMELS FROM ENGLAND. (½)

[See p. 103.

results of analysis are as follows, and an analysis of Mont Beuvray enamel is here given for comparison :—

TARA HILL.		MONT BEUVRAY.	
Silica	43·28	Silica	42·89
Lead oxide . . .	32·85	Lead oxide . . .	28·30
Potassium and calcium		Tin oxide . . .	2·25
oxides, with loss .	1·44	Lime	8·28
Aluminium and iron		Alumina . . .	2·75
oxides . . .	2·75	Oxide of iron . .	2·45
Cuprous oxide . .	9·86	Cuprous oxide . .	6·41
Soda	9·82	Soda (by diff.) . .	6·67
	100·00		100·00

The melting-point was found to be 686° C., and it melts to a dark-green transparent glass. The mass may be regarded as fused material that had been prepared for red enamel to be used cold, as studs attached by pins (as fig. 125).

It should be noticed that the enamel does not monopolize the surface, but that broad bands of the bronze ground are left, to combine with the colour in peculiar designs that are remarkable for their grace and freedom. Though the metal seems to have been blackened in one of the specimens illustrated (plate VIII, no. 3), it must be borne in mind that the bronze was generally of a golden colour (as no. 2), which would enhance the splendour of such artistic products as the Thames and Witham shields. In the first or second century of our era, other colours were introduced (blue, orange, green, yellow, and brown), and specimens are shown with blue (no. 4) or blue and white, in addition to red (as no. 1) : this innovation was, doubtless, due to contact with Roman civilization, and enamelled brooches of S-form, showing the transition, are exhibited in the Room of Roman Britain. The designs about the same time undergo a change, but perhaps only in the area most completely Romanized ; and Keltic scrolls with enamel sometimes appear on objects of Roman style, as a gold bracelet from a hoard of the second century found at Rhayader, Radnorshire (Guide to Roman Britain, pl. III).

Most of the early British enamels are on horse-trappings (plate VIII), and only one or two pieces at all similar are to be seen in continental museums. Nothing is known of the history of a piece at Florence resembling no. 2. But that the examples illustrated are not exceptional in our own country is proved by the existence of several pieces like no. 1 in this and other collections ; by another somewhat like no. 2 at Norwich, and by a bridle-bit from Birrenswark, Dumfries, almost identical with no. 4 (Rise, near Hull). Factories producing enamels of another kind have been discovered at Pompeii (before A.D. 79) and Mont Beuvray (the ancient Bibracte), an important site in the Dépt. Saône-et-Loire, where Caesar mentions a general gathering of the Gaulish tribes in the year 52 B. C. That part of Bibracte in which the workshops were situated was destroyed by fire before the Christian era, and the enamels found there, all of

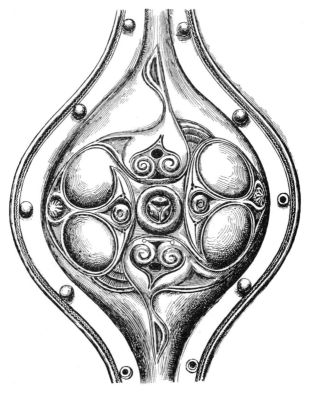

Fig. 114.—Shield from the Witham, central boss. ($\frac{1}{2}$)

red colour, may safely be classified as Gaulish or Keltic. A little later the new style of Roman imperial times was introduced, in which various colours were arranged within adjoining panels on the surface to be decorated, and all the metal visible between the enamelled spaces consisted of narrow strips that kept the colours apart, but were no longer an integral part of the design. The British enamellers seem to have retained their own methods for a while after the Claudian conquest, but the influence of Rome may be noticed in the decoration of the Embleton sword. The form of the blade and scabbard is native British, and the enamel on the handle is not used in conjunction with scroll-work (p. 103), but is arranged in rows of rectangular spaces filled with alternate colours. This latter was the method employed in the decoration of bronze horse-trappings found near Neath, Glamorganshire (p. 164).

The transition from coral to enamel is well illustrated by important pieces in this collection (Cases 32, 33). Though shields

Fig. 115.—Shield from the Witham, lower disc. ($\frac{1}{2}$)

of the early Britons are rarely found, there is enough material to show the various stages of development which, by reference to the Continent, may be approximately dated. Style, form, and decoration combine to prove that the Witham shield (figs. 113–15) is the earliest of its kind in Britain, and contrasts strongly with the circular bucklers of the Bronze Age (Prehistoric Room). The boar, which may here be recognized by the rivet-holes and difference in colour round the outline, is here distorted to fit the space, but was long a favourite emblem among the Keltic peoples

(p. 147).   The pointed oval boss and thin central rib appear on an oval shield (43 in. × 25½ in.) in the well-known statue of the ' Dying Gaul ', which belonged to a series executed about 240–230 B. C. to commemorate Greek victories over the Gauls in Asia Minor.   The Witham shield is about 1 in. longer, but 10 in. narrower, and though without the classical border, is engraved with designs (fig. 115) that are evidently derived from the Greek palmette (as fig. 13).   In view of further developments in Britain, we may look upon the circular ornaments at the ends as a native feature, but for the same reason we must assign this specimen to the second century B.C.   Too much stress must not be laid on the Grimthorpe shield, which is exhibited in what was probably its original form, the length being about 36 in.; but there is an evident connexion between this Witham mounting and the fragment found in the Thames near Wandsworth, and now mounted in the same Case.   The embossed work is slightly different in style, and to all appearance later, while there is but little engraving on this fragment, which evidently had a circular ornament at both ends of the central rib.   By analogy, the length of the shield would have been 33 or 34 in.   The tendency seems to have been for the edges to acquire a double curve, and for the terminal discs to approach the centre, where the pointed oval expanded into a circular boss with broad flat edging.   The intermediate stage may be represented by the Grimthorpe shield, though the ornament is there much simpler.   A shield-boss, engraved and embossed, was found with the fragment already referred to in the Thames near Wandsworth, but association in such circumstances is poor evidence of contemporary date; and the circular mount is evidently from a shield like the enamelled example from the Thames near Battersea (plate I).   Here the terminal discs have approached the centre, and the connecting rib is nearly eliminated, the entire length of the shield being 14 in. less than the Witham example.   Moreover, the style of decoration is different: the embossed portions, which in the earlier piece are rotund in section and enriched by engraving, have become more sharp and slender, the pattern more symmetrical and linear, and the coral replaced by red discs of enamel.   Open-work bronze wings enclosing a swastika were fixed by a central pin to a clay button, on which enamel was fused (not applied cold as at Bugthorpe, p. 114).   This, then, is not strictly *cloisonné* or cell-work, but a substitution of red enamel buttons for coral ; and the absence of other colours confirms the opinion that the shield was made within a few years of the birth of Christ.   The next important change seems to be illustrated by the Polden Hill find (p. 143), which included bronze shield-bosses of the type found in the Danish mosses.   These seem to be of the native pattern in use during the first century of the Roman domination in Britain and, except for their slightly

conical form, are in fact not unlike the true Roman pattern, as
that from Kirkham, Lancashire. The model of an oval shield has
been found at Hod Hill; and round shields appear on the British
coinage.

With the possible exception of those from Ogmore Down,
Glamorganshire (now lost), the two bronze helmets in the collection are the only British examples known, and both exhibit a
peculiar method of enamelling (p. 102), bosses being deeply scored
to key the red enamel. Both also have embossed work, not quite

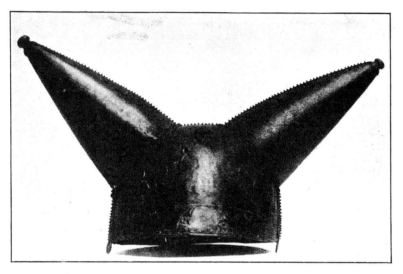

Fig. 116.—Bronze helmet, Thames at Waterloo Bridge. ($\frac{1}{4}$)

in the same style, the horned specimen from the Thames (fig. 116)
being rather slight and ineffective compared with the other (fig. 65),
which has a broad neck-guard, and was probably found in the north
of England.   The latter evidently had a knob at the summit, the
rivet-holes remaining, and in this respect resembled the usual
Italian type of early classical times.   Examples from Etruria of
the fifth and later centuries B.C. may be seen in the Room of
Greek and Roman Life, but it is unlikely that the British specimens are earlier than the Christian era.   The broad neck-guard
was a feature of Roman helmets (example from Tring, Herts., in
Room of Roman Britain), and like them the British specimen
probably had cheek-pieces ; but the horned helmet had no knob or
neck-guard, and was apparently fastened by a chin-strap. Helmets
with similar horn-like projections are represented on the Roman

arch at Orange (Vaucluse), dating from A. D. 21 ; but this is the only specimen found north of the Alps.

Swords of the Early Iron Age are but rarely found in the British Isles, and, as might be expected, include few early types. Some examples of La Tène II have come from the Thames, fairly well preserved, with tapering point and ogee-guard on the sword, and a loop near the mouth of the metal scabbard.   Two scabbards in Case 18 are worthy of special notice, as being good copies of an unusually long type generally found in Switzerland, and rarely elsewhere.   That from Corroy, Marne, exhibited in Case 16, long and unwieldy as it is, measures 4 in. less than the Thames specimen (plate IX, no. 4), which shows the transverse bands and heart-shaped chape of its prototype.   Somewhat later in style, but of the same type, is that from the Thames at Amerden (plate IX,

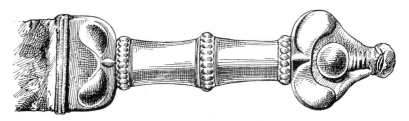

Fig. 117.—Bronze sword-hilt, Worton, Lancs. ($\frac{2}{3}$)

no. 6), which is ornamented at the mouth with applied open-work and engraved basket-pattern ; while an S-scroll takes the place of a transverse band.   Another Thames specimen (plate IX, no. 7) represents the closing period of La Tène, with its blunt point and absence of chape : the two bars near the mouth being of the pattern also seen on the scabbard illustrated from La Tène (plate IX, no. 3), and on the Somme Bionne specimen itself.   But the ogee-curve did not disappear from the sword in the period that may be called La Tène IV.   The Sadberge (Haughton-le-Skerne) sword shows that the mount at the mouth of the scabbard was trans-ferred to the base of the grip, where it appears in the form of a cocked hat.   The same feature occurs on an enamelled specimen found at Rudstone, East Riding, Yorkshire (York Museum), and on a sword-handle from Worton (fig. 117), which is a solid bronze casting.   The Embleton specimen shows the same peculiarity in a less pronounced form ; but loose mounts from the mouth of the scabbard have been preserved, one from Brough Castle being of open-work (fig. 118).

The British development of the La Tène sword is marked by two novelties of form, which occur together on the fine example from Cotterdale (plate IX, no. 9).   The loop for suspension is placed half-way down the back (or front) of the scabbard, where it is supported by ornamental ribs expanding into open-work at the mouth. Examples are shown from Sadberge, Stanwick, Embleton, and Worton. The derivation of the chape is not obvious, but what may have been the prototype was found in Pilling Moss, Lancs. (Salford Museum), the binding of the scabbard terminating in two thin discs placed side by side at right angles to the plane of the sword. It would have been quite in keeping with what we know of Keltic artificers to emphasize and expand these discs, as on the Embleton, Cotterdale, and Stanwick examples—that from Sadberge has probably lost a chape of this description. The chape of a scabbard from the Tweed near Carham (plate IX, no. 2) seems to be an exaggerated form of that on fig. 124.

Light is thrown on the chronology of Danes Graves and similar sites in Yorkshire by the discovery of an anthropoid sword (like fig. 58, no. 3) with a long sword of La Tène II type in an un-burnt burial at North Grimston. Another, complete but poorly preserved, is published from Ripon, and these render it almost certain that Lord Londesborough's specimen (fig. 58, no. 3) was

Fig. 118.—Scabbard mount, Brough Castle, Westmorland. (¼)

also found in Yorkshire, as he lived in the county and excavated locally. With them may be mentioned a dagger found with its sheath in the river Witham, Lincolnshire, the head in this case being replaced by a complete imp-like figure in the fork of the pommel. Another dagger of this type, from Southwark, is in the Guildhall Museum, London ; and all so far found in England have a human head, except the imperfect example exhibited from the Avon at Sea Mills near Bristol, and the complete dagger with bronze sheath from Ham Hill, Somerset (Taunton Museum), both of which are more akin to fig. 58, no. 2. It should be added that the Ham Hill dagger came from a burial after cremation, possibly of Belgic origin (p. 11).

The series of daggers is less complete, but the Thames has yielded several that exhibit continental traits. Perhaps the earliest is that without its chape, but with tang to the blade and a bronze plate on the front of the scabbard ornamented with raised dots and running into a fish-tail form at the point. Whatever its actual date of manufacture, this specimen seems to afford a clue to the evolution of one from Chelsea, which has a semicircular finial (plate IX, no. 1). It is conceivable that a gradual lengthening of the crescent produced the type which is represented by two examples from the Thames at Wandsworth (fig. 119) and Battersea, the latter being somewhat later in style, to judge from the parallel development of sword-scabbards (p. 58).   A further stage is marked by the pearled open-work chape of the Richmond dagger, the blade of which is curved in a fashion recalling the Roman pattern (two from Hod Hill, Case 23).   The same curved blade is seen in the remarkable dagger and sheath, evidently belonging together, from the Thames at Cookham, but this and a finely

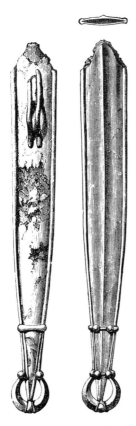

Fig. 119.—Dagger-sheath, Thames at Wandsworth.   ($\frac{1}{3}$)

Fig. 120.—Dagger-sheath, Thames at Wandsworth.   ($\frac{1}{2}$)

decorated scabbard from Wandsworth (fig. 120) are difficult to classify.

Though there seem to be no exact parallels to continental spear-heads in this country, the Museum possesses several examples from the Thames that may safely be attributed to the pre-Roman period, and one or two that appear to be copied from a Bronze Age type. Their principal characteristic is the entire socket for the shaft, which contrasts with the split socket of the Anglo-Saxon

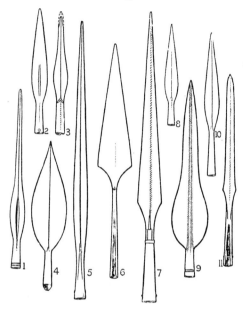

Fig. 121.—Spear-heads of Early Iron Age. ($\frac{1}{8}$)

period ; and while the shape of the earlier blades varies indefinitely, Saxon examples belong to a few well-defined types. The group here illustrated (fig. 121) includes two specimens with split sockets (nos. 6 and 11), which are exceptions to the rule ; three specimens from the Marne district (nos. 2, 8, 10), the first of which has two grooves at the centre, much like one from the Thames (no. 1) ; and one well-preserved head from La Tène itself (no. 9), with the blade widened below. The curved edges of the last are characteristic, and an imperfect example from the same site is exhibited with the irregular wavy outline seen on several extant (p. 48). The remainder are from the Thames at London, and include one broad leaf-shaped specimen (no. 4), a long slender pattern (no. 5), and angular forms (nos. 6 and 7), which are not uncommon from the

Thames.   Some of those illustrated have collars or engraved lines below the blade for additional strength or ornament (nos. 1, 7, 9), and most were fastened to the shaft by a peg through the sockets, seen in no. 11.   A few iron ferrules for the butt of the spear, some of unusual length, are exhibited with the spear-heads.

The principal types utilized for dating purposes having been discussed, the scheme may now be applied to the more important grave-finds on exhibition.   In this country, apart from exceptional cases (as fig. 84), iron makes its first appearance in unburnt burials, like those at Arras (p. 115), and geographical names have been cited in support of the hypothesis that the new-comers (Brythons or P Kelts) were from north-east France.   The head-forms are, however, so far inconclusive (below), and it should be pointed out that Arras in Gaul was in the territory of the Belgic Atrebates, who were apparently located south of the Thames in Britain ; further, the Parisii in Gaul belonged to the central Keltic area, and their presence in Yorkshire (certified by Ptolemy) cannot be said to prove a close connexion between the burials of the Wolds and the Champagne.

The longitudinal index of certain skulls from Iron Age burials in Yorkshire—Arras, 74 ; Danes Graves, 74–73 ; Grimthorpe, 71 —is fairly uniform, and shows a long-headed population sharply separated from the occupants of the Round barrows, whose average index is 81–83 (*Bronze Age Guide*, p. 18).   At first sight we might attribute the population during the centuries imme-diately preceding the Roman conquest to a fresh immigration from the Continent, but Canon Greenwell suggested another explana-tion, that this difference of skull-form might be due to the fact that the intruding short-headed people of the Round barrows were gradually absorbed by the earlier and more numerous race whom they had overcome.   The subdued population may at first have been kept in a servile condition, and not as a rule interred with their masters in the barrows ; but as time went on, and intermingling of the two peoples became common, a change would gradually take place in the racial characteristics, and the features of the numerically stronger people would predominate.   The Iron Age type of skull in Yorkshire would therefore approximate to the neolithic type, which is there markedly dolichocephalic (index 70–71, against the modern English 79).   Prof. William Wright, who examined a number of skulls from Danes Graves, thinks this a plausible theory, and suggests the alternative that they belonged to settlers from the Continent more or less identical in race with the long-headed neolithic population of Britain, but who had become a mixed race before reaching our shores.   The average of seven female skulls he found to be 74, that of fifteen males being 73 ; and these measurements are con-firmed by those of twelve from the same site in the museum of the Royal College of Surgeons : average (probably of both sexes) 73·5.

In Yorkshire there are chariot-burials that closely resemble those dating from La Tène I in Dépt. Marne ; and the same type of pottery occurs in this Gaulish area about 300 years before it is used for cremated burials at Aylesford, in the first century B. C. In the interval, the funeral customs in north-east France had evidently undergone a complete change, while the sepulchral pottery retained certain of the ancient forms. This may mean nothing more than that the Gaulish potter made vessels of a customary pattern, and that the Belgic German, equally observant of tradition, used those same vessels as cinerary urns for the dead of his own race. It is a fair deduction that the natives of this part of Gaul carried on many of their old traditions, but that the

Fig. 122.—Bone arrow-head, Grimthorpe, E. R. Yorks. ($\frac{2}{3}$)

foreign custom of cremation was established in their country by a dominant people from beyond the Rhine.

An interment of much interest was discovered in 1868 at Grimthorpe, near Pocklington, East Riding of Yorks. There was no barrow on the site, but a hollow was observed in the top of a chalk-pit, and found to contain a human skull. Further examination revealed a human skeleton lying in an oval grave 4$\frac{1}{2}$ ft. long, at a depth of 4 ft. It was in the contracted position, on its left side, with the head to the south-west. The body had been wrapped in the skins of animals, probably goats, with the hairy side inwards, and these were fastened by a number of skewers made of the metatarsal bones of the goat. The impression of short, fine hair was noticed on the bronze face of the scabbard ; several bone points, which were pierced at the butt, and in one case retained a transverse wooden peg, may originally have been used as arrowheads and mounted on wooden shafts (fig. 122). On the breast were the metallic remains of a shield or buckler, and it was observed that the plates were so situated that its diameter cannot have been more than 12 in. This, however, can only apply to the breadth of the shield, as the two semi-cylindrical rods, which are perfect as regards their length, evidently belonged to it, and were found the one near the head, the other about the knees of the skeleton. This is not precise enough to fix the entire length ; but if the rods were fixed on the front above and below the boss, the minimum length would be about 27 in., comparing well with the Thames example (30¼ in.). This analogy suggests that the small disc found with rivets below the shield was one of two fixed at either end of the shield as finials to the rods ; and the fact that the top end of the grave was the first to attract attention might account for the loss of a second disc, which would be on a level with the skull. The mounts, of which the decoration is noticed elsewhere (p. 106), are exhibited in the positions they seem to have occupied on the wood or leather body of the shield (Case 32). The thickness of the material can be determined, by the length of the rivet still remaining, to have been ⅜ in.

On the left side of the skeleton lay the remains of a spear-head and a two-edged iron sword in its sheath (fig. 123), the entire length being 29 in. The handle retains on an iron tang two oval iron plates between which a grip of wood was inserted, the space beyond at both ends being covered by bone or horn which has

FIG. 123.—Sword in scabbard, Grimthorpe. (⅑)

disappeared. The blade springs from a short curved bronze guard, the ends of which have transverse iron rods, recalling rivets in a similar position on the long Thames sword in Case 18. The face of the scabbard was of bronze, the back of iron, but both had a central ridge, and the mouth was probably curved to fit into the guard (as fig. 124). In yet another respect this sword resembles that from Bugthorpe, the heavy moulded chape of bronze being of the same type in both, but the Grimthorpe specimen being the earlier of the two. Studs were also found in the Grimthorpe grave closely resembling those in position on fig. 124, and undoubted coral was recovered.

The skull was recovered in a remarkably perfect state, and proved to be that of a man about thirty years of age. It was unusually narrow, long and tall, with a long narrow face, prominent aquiline nose, and square chin. The cephalic index is calculated to be 71, dolichocephalic subjects in general ranging between 70 and 75, and the average index of Englishmen at the present day being nearly 79.

The sword-sheath from Bugthorpe, E. R. Yorks., is finely engraved though much rubbed ; and the curved mouth should be noticed as a characteristic of La Tène II. With it were found two discs (fig. 125) which have studs of red enamel treated like coral and attached by pins passing through the centre. The burial to which all belonged can therefore be dated before the general use of sunk enamel (champlevé).

Important excavations were made in 1815–17 by the Rev. E. W.

Stillingfleet and others on a spur of the Yorkshire wolds, about three miles east of Market Weighton, East Riding. A group of barrows, about ninety in number, was almost bisected by the road from York to Beverley, the farm north of the road being known as Arras, that to the south, Hessleskew. Beyond the barrows, in different directions, were single and double dykes or earthworks, no doubt thrown up for defensive purposes; and enclosing one of the barrows was a square fosse, the sides of which corresponded with the cardinal points. The barrows were circular, and for the most part of small size and elevation, in some cases almost escaping observation. Nearly every barrow contained a human skeleton, deposited in a shallow cist or cavity in the chalk, in a contracted position, the head, in all but one or two cases, lying to the north. No coins or weapons, and scarcely any

FIG. 124.—Bronze sword-sheath, Bugthorpe, E. R. Yorks. ($\frac{1}{4}$ and $\frac{1}{3}$)

FIG. 125.—Disc with enamel studs, Bugthorpe. ($\frac{2}{3}$)

implements, were found in the graves, while the comparative abundance of ornaments also suggests that most were the graves of women. In several instances, the bones of the fore-arm were found encircled by bronze bracelets, and one skeleton had in addition a bronze ring round the bones of the leg (p. 67). Another was found with a torc of bronze in position on the neck. It is unfortunate that a complete record was kept of only three of the barrows opened at that period, but these were of exceptional

FIG. 126.—Bronze bracelet, Cowlam, E. R., Yorks. ($\frac{1}{1}$)

FIG. 127.—Bronze brooch, Cowlam. ($\frac{1}{1}$)

interest and importance, and the contents may be seen in York Museum.

In Case 18 are a few ornaments from two barrows in a group at Cowlam, E. Riding, excavated by Canon Greenwell. The first was 22 ft. in diameter, 2 ft. high, and made up of chalk rubble. At the centre, on the natural surface, was the body of an aged woman laid upon the left side, with the head north-east and the hands up to the face. On the right wrist was the bronze bracelet (fig. 126) exhibited, and near the chin the bronze brooch (fig. 127). Its pin had been originally of bronze in one piece with the spiral coil, but had been replaced by one of iron, fastened at one end into a piece of wood inserted in the spiral coil. The brooch itself is of La Tène I type. At the neck were seventy dark-blue glass beads with sunk patterns filled with white ; and part of a shale bracelet, together with a large number of sherds, was found with a few flint chippings in the material of the mound.

The second barrow was of chalk rubble, 24 ft. in diameter and 1 ft. high, having on the south side a trench running east and west, 5 ft. long, $1\frac{3}{4}$ ft. wide, and 3 ft. deep. In the mound were several fragments of pottery, together with broken bones of several oxen, of a goat or sheep, of two pigs, and two horses. At the centre, on the natural surface, was the body of a middle-aged

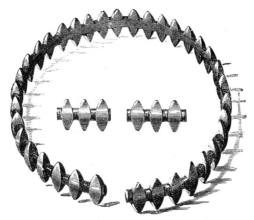

FIG. 128.—Bronze bracelet, Cowlam. ($\frac{1}{1}$)

woman, laid on the left side, with the head north and the hands up to the face. On the right wrist was a toothed bracelet (fig. 128) that has a remarkable 'patina'. The body had been much contracted, and occupied altogether a space of 35 in. Immediately to the west of, and extending partly underneath the body, was a hollow, 7 ft. by 4 ft., and 3 ft. deep, in which were flint chippings, charcoal, fragments of dark and hard-backed pottery, and many broken bones of four oxen, one goat or sheep, and one young horse.

It is said that before the wolds were enclosed, there were as many as 500 barrows, called collectively Danes Graves, at Kilham, about four miles north of Driffield, East Riding Yorkshire. Fourteen opened by Canon Greenwell in 1864 were all of small size, 16–24 ft. in diameter and 2–4 ft. high, formed of chalk rubble. In all these barrows, and in some examined on other occasions, the interment had been made in an oblong hollow cut in the original

I

surface, the bodies being without coffins, and as a rule so much doubled up that they must have been tightly swathed. The hands were placed upon the chin, but the bodies lay indifferently on the right or left side, though the majority had the head at the north end of the grave. In three cases a hand-made urn, full of small stones and about 5 in. in height, had been placed close behind the head. The most remarkable interment was that of a man, laid upon his right side, with the head at the west end. Lying close to the mouth and discolouring the teeth, was found a loop of iron 4 in. long, much corroded, probably a brooch. On each side of the body was placed a goat, their heads also to the west. Goats have also been found in a barrow six miles north of Pickering in the North Riding, and at Therfield, near Royston, Herts. The bodies were much more contracted than in the Round barrows of the

Fig. 129.—Pottery from Danes Graves, E. R. Yorks. (⅕)

district, and the graves were massed together as in a modern churchyard, not isolated as in the Bronze period. Further, the skulls were not brachycephalic, but, according to Dr. Thurnam, had an average index of 73 ; while the iron fragment and a bronze bracelet (the latter found about 1830 in another grave, with a jet bracelet and an iron 'comb'), suggest the Early Iron Age, to which must also be referred five plain pottery vases, found containing bones of the pig (fig. 129).

The small brooch with 'broken back' (fig. 130) also came from this cemetery, and belongs to a type peculiar to Britain. The head of the pin has two loops, one bent back on the other to enclose a loop at the end of the bow, all being held together by an inserted tube like an eyelet. In type it illustrates the transition from La Tène I–II, but is probably later in date. The iron brooch adjoining came from the same site, but is not well preserved.

Excavation has shown that the term ' Danes Graves ', both here and elsewhere in the country, has no historical justification. The large number of mounds here and at Arras (three miles east of Market Weighton) indicate that the community, possibly Parisii from Gaul, had occupied the neighbourhood for a considerable time, and the cephalic index again points to a dolichocephalic race, the average being 75 (male) and 71 (female). The absence of weapons of any kind from the interments at Arras and Danes Graves may indicate peaceful occupation of the district, but it is conceivable that the inhabitants had been disarmed or had a better use for their weapons. The occurrence of actual buckles in the latter cemetery would render it probable that some at least of these graves were not earlier than the Christian era. Though examples are known from the remarkable cemetery of Koban in the Caucasus (p. 85), the buckle, as distinct from the penannular brooch, was not generally known in the West before the Roman period.

In spite of a general resemblance, it was noticed that the Arras graves contained many ornaments, no pottery, and the skeleton sometimes extended; whereas the Danes Graves burials were contracted, contained food and pottery, but very few ornaments.

In Cases 18, 19 are exhibited remains from two chariot-burials in Yorkshire. One was discovered at Arras in 1877 near the site explored by Mr. Stillingfleet in 1815–17, and was described by Canon Greenwell. Under a small barrow, 14 ft. in diameter and $1\frac{1}{2}$ ft. high, a grave had been sunk in the chalk-rock, of circular form, 12 ft. across and 3 ft. deep. In it was the skeleton of a muscular woman between thirty-five

FIG. 130.—Bronze brooch with details, Danes Graves. ($\frac{1}{1}$)

and forty years of age, probably laid at full length. Behind the head were the bones of the forepart of two pigs, and below the head a mirror of iron, $6\frac{3}{4}$ in. across and 13 in. long with the handle, which had bronze mounts at each end: in size and shape very like one found during the previous explorations. At the back of the body were laid two wheels slightly overlapping, the tires having a diameter of 34 in. and a width of about $1\frac{1}{2}$ in. The naves were bound with two bronze hoops over 5 in. in diameter and $1\frac{3}{4}$ in. wide with a raised rib along the centre, but the metal was too thin to give any additional strength. No other part of the chariot seems to have been interred, but in front of the chest were the two bronze snaffle-bits, about $9\frac{1}{2}$ in. long, and apparently made of iron coated with bronze. In the earth thrown out of the grave a 'terret' of bronze was subsequently found, like examples from Hagbourne Hill (p. 88).

The other chariot-burial was at Beverley, and was opened by Canon Greenwell in 1875. Here the only articles discovered were those now exhibited, there being no bones of man or beast, though such might easily have decayed in such a soil.   Two iron chariot-wheels lay side by side, each with its nave-band at the centre.   The iron tires and bridle-bits have been distorted and swollen with rust, but there can be no doubt of their date and origin.   The diameter of the wheels was about 28 in., considerably smaller than the Arras and Somme Bionne specimens.

A few typical glass beads are exhibited in Case 18 : those from the first Cowlam barrow (fig. 131) show white zigzag markings inlaid in cobalt blue, and only one of the seventy had white annulets, like those from the Queen's barrow at Arras; others from the latter cemetery are shown without the white inlay, which has fallen out.   Similar beads are common abroad in the period of La Tène, and the rings are supposed to have served as amulets against the evil eye.

In La Tène II the rings give place to spirals, and in the next stage the beads are much larger and polychrome.   It is clear that

FIG. 131.—Glass beads, England and Ireland.   ($\frac{2}{3}$)

the Yorkshire specimens were imported, but the exact place of manufacture is not at present known, though Egypt, Phoenicia, and Marseilles have been suggested for glass bracelets of La Tène II and III.

Prof. Buckman, in 1851, analysed a specimen of the numerous beads of blue glass discovered in the Iron Age barrows of Yorkshire. It was of a Prussian blue colour, with three circular grooves round the circumference filled with white paste.   It fused only at a very high temperature, a fact explained by the absence of lead in its composition ; and was found to contain silica, potash, soda, oxide of iron, a small quantity of alumina, traces of lime and magnesia, and oxide of copper.   This last was used as colouring matter, and according to the method of combining and manipu-lating it, is capable of producing yellow, ruby, green, and blues of various shades.   Cobalt does not seem to have been used.

The Arras mirror (p. 119) is not of the usual type found in this country, and details of some in the collection may here be added. That from Trelan Bahow (fig. 132) is typical of the series and is of bronze, made in two pieces, and ornamented at the back with engraved scroll-work enclosed in two circles.   It is remarkable that all these mirrors are decorated in the same style, the basket-

pattern (p. 99) being freely used as a filling. The Cornish specimen was found in 1833 with bronze bracelets, other rings of
uncertain use, and two glass beads, all in one of several interments
that were protected by covering-stones and other slabs set on edge
all round.

A larger mirror of this type (drawing in Case 27) was found in
1879 at Birdlip, near Gloucester, on the edge of the Cotswold
hills. Three bodies had been interred in a continuous line, with
the feet to the south, and
whitewashed slabs of stone
had been placed round and
above them to form rough
tombs or cists. The two
outer skeletons belonged to
adult males, but had no
grave-furniture, while between them had been
buried a woman in the
prime of life, with a re-
markable series of bronzes.
Besides the oval mirror,
which measures $9\frac{3}{4} \times 10\frac{5}{8}$ in.
without the handle, and
weighs $38\frac{1}{4}$ oz., there was a
circular bowl, 9 in. in diameter, hammered very thin,
and provided with a rim
skilfully turned on the
lathe. It lay on the face,
and was accompanied by
another bowl of similar
make but smaller dimen-
sions ($3\frac{1}{2}$ in. at the mouth).
With the bones lay a fine
silver-gilt brooch with
spiral spring, pierced catch-

FIG 132.—Back of bronze mirror, Trelan
Bahow, St. Keverne, Cornwall. ($\frac{1}{3}$)

plate, and hook on the bow, recalling the eye-brooch (*Augenfibel*,
see *Guide to Roman Britain*, fig. 65) which has been assigned
to the first half of the first century after Christ. There were
also four small bronze rings with an inside diameter of about
$\frac{7}{10}$ in., a tubular bronze bracelet closing with a slight spring,
and the handles of a key and knife, the latter terminating in
an animal's head not unlike that in Taunton Museum, and
having two eye-sockets for settings resembling those on the collar
from Weymouth (Case 60) and the Aust statuette (fig. 173). Of
sixteen beads found, most were of amber, the largest of which
were $1\frac{1}{2}$ in. across, while two were of jet and there was one

specimen of grey marble.   Similar beads have frequently been found in Britain.

The associated objects at Birdlip point to the second half of the first century A. D., and this date is confirmed by the discovery at Mount Batten, Plymouth, of a mirror, with brooches similar to the largest of a Roman group exhibited from Lancing, Sussex.   It should be noted that in none of these cases had the body been cremated, and it seems that in the non-Belgic area of Britain the native population buried their dead unburnt, though the Roman fashion at this time was to deposit the ashes in cinerary urns.

A rival to the Birdlip mirror is exhibited in Case 30 (pl. X). It was found in 1908 during excavations for ironstone west of Desborough, Northants, and nothing was noticed in association with it, though comparison with Birdlip suggests a woman's burial.   It is in better condition and more graceful than the Gloucester specimen in spite of the latter's enamel decoration. The reflecting surface is of kidney form with a major axis of $10\frac{1}{4}$ in., and the finely moulded handle is 6 in. long.   On the back (fig. 133) eccentric scrolls of the usual character are engraved with basket-pattern filling, the design filling the space to a nicety and closely resembling that of Birdlip.   When found it was entirely covered with a light green patina ; but a calcareous concretion on the face was removed with acid, which restored the reflecting surface to its original golden colour.

It should be observed that these and most of our other bronzes were found well away from the south-east of England ; and yet the graves of Yorkshire and the brooches of Wiltshire, for instances, are earlier than the cremated burials and imported bronzes of the coastal districts nearest Gaul.   The former belong to La Tène I and II, the latter to La Tène III ; and either series incompletely represents the second half of the Early Iron Age.   The brooches inland date for the most part before the Belgic conquest of north-east Gaul, whereas these found in Kent are contemporary with the pedestal cinerary urns and may be referred to the Belgae whose arrival was not long before Caesar's invasion.   Dr. Cyril Fox has observed that the area of ' Belgic ' culture marked by the Aylesford type of urn and cremation is not coterminous with that of tribes known to be of Belgic origin.   It includes the counties of Kent, Essex, Middlesex, Hertford, Buckingham, Southern Bedford, and Southern Cambridge ; but may prove to extend farther westward.

For his report on the Swarling cemetery (p. 131) Mr. Bushe-Fox went into the question of a Belgic invasion, and rejected a landing in force about 200 B. C., in favour of gradual penetration between 100 and 60 B. C. which would account for the finds in Kent and Essex.   The Belgae of the West of England (Winchester was *Venta Belgarum*) would on this hypothesis be later arrivals who

PLATE X. BACK OF BRONZE MIRROR, DESBOROUGH. (L. 13³/₄ in.)

[*See* p. 122.

PLATE XI. SILVER CUPS AND BRONZE MASKS, WELWYN, HERTS. (about 1/2)

[See p. 132.

PLATE XII. IRON FRAME AND FIRE-DOGS, WELWYN, HERTS.

[*See* p. 132.

PLATE XIII. SERIES OF ANCIENT BRITISH COINS. ($^1/_1$)

[*See* p. 166.

passed inland because their kinsmen, the Cantii and Trinobantes, were already in possession of the coast. It used to be thought that the British coinage began about 150 B.C. and dated the

Fig. 133.—Back of bronze mirror, Desborough, Northants. ($\frac{1}{3}$)

Belgic arrival; but it is now held that the early (uninscribed) coins were minted in Gaul and only came here by way of trade, the native coinage beginning after 54 B.C. The inland people may perhaps be called Brythons: there is less doubt about the nationality of the cremationists nearer Gaul. It will now be convenient

to consider the contents of two cemeteries that may with some
confidence be referred to the Belgae of the first century B.C.

The most important of the Aylesford discoveries was made in
1886, when the removal of the surface soil revealed a pit-burial
(fig. 134) containing the bucket (*cista*), the flagon (*oenochoè*), the
skillet of frying-pan shape (*patella*), and the three brooches (*fibulae*)

Fig. 134.—Vertical section of grave, Aylesford, Kent.

exhibited in Case K. All were of bronze, and lay mingled with
calcined bones and fragments of pottery vases in a circular grave
about $3\frac{1}{2}$ ft. deep, the bottom and side of which had been coated
with a chalky compound. The bucket contained burnt bones and
the brooches, while the flagon and skillet lay outside it, as shown
in fig. 134. Some of the accompanying earthenware vessels had
been used as cinerary urns, and have since been restored.

The importance of this richly furnished burial, in conjunction
with others discovered on the site, was fully appreciated by Sir

Arthur Evans, who made investigations on the spot and published
an elaborate account of the cemetery.   The bronze vessels of the
principal interment may first be dealt with, as affording the
strongest evidence of intercourse with the Continent.   Something

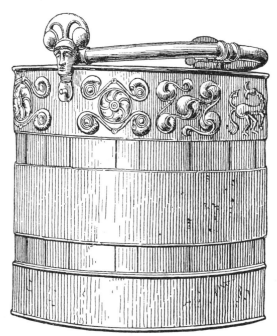

FIG. 135.—Bronze-mounted bucket, Aylesford.   ($\frac{1}{4}$)

FIG. 136.—Embossed frieze of bucket, Aylesford.   ($\frac{1}{4}$)

has already been said (p. 27) with regard to the ancestry of the
bronze-mounted bucket (fig. 135), and the development of its ornament (fig. 136) from the classical palmette has been shown above
(p. 19).   It consists of a framework of wooden staves bound with
thin metal bands attached by rivets, each of the staves being
1·4 in. wide.   The bands were three in number, 2·7 in. wide,

leaving two bare interstices ; and the total height of the vessel was
10 in., the diameter being about half an inch greater. The hooped
handle is of iron plated with bronze, and is movable ; but the
mode of attachment to the ornamental plates on the brim is
peculiar. In the classical examples from which it is evidently
copied, the handles are double, and work in two round holes
(fig. 24), which are here represented by the circular bosses above
the temples, the ends of the handle being somewhat clumsily
inserted behind the head. The ornamental bands are retained in
a debased form, but the Keltic workman would be unequal to
the task of reproducing the claw-feet.

The flagon found in the same grave is of Italo-Greek manufac-

FIG. 137.—Bronze jug, with detail,
Aylesford. ($\frac{1}{4}$ and $\frac{1}{2}$)

ture, and not merely the
barbarous imitation of a
classical model. The beaked
flagon (*Schnabelkanne*) of the
Somme Bionne type (fig. 53)
seems to have passed out of
fashion about 300 B. C., giving
place to flagons of the kind
here represented ; it is interesting to contrast the ornamentation below the handle
of the later form (fig. 137)
with the classical palmette
which it is doubtless intended
to represent. In the extensive
cemetery near Lake Mag-
giore, called San Bernardo,
which contains no graves
earlier than about 234 B. C.,
specimens of this type are
common, and in one grave at
least occurred with a skillet and brooch almost identical with
those from Aylesford, together with Roman coins of 149–144 B. C.
Though hundreds of similar flagons have been found at Pompeii,
Dr. Willers remarks on the absence of skillets there, and would
refer our example to upper Italy, regarding it as Gaulish work of
the early second century B. C.

Nor is this the only parallel in the Ticino cemetery. A tankard
with an open-work handle (like fig. 146), closely resembles the
Aylesford specimen now restored (fig. 139), and was found in
a grave with coins dating from 119–114 B. C. Though the feet of
the Aylesford brooches (fig. 138) are imperfect or wanting, there
can be no doubt as to the close relation between them and specimens
from San Bernardo, another of which was found with a coin
of 144 B. C. But, all things considered, the date of the Aylesford

cemetery was about the time of Caesar's invasion. Gold coins from the site are noticed below (p. 168).

The pottery found with the bronze vessels at Aylesford evidently belongs to types well represented in the cemetery, and may be included in a general description (p. 129). The three brooches of bronze contained in the bucket present some difficulties, and all were unfortunately damaged. The largest is hard to classify as the foot is wanting, and the form of the bow with a collar near the foot is unusual. The other two are a pair, and though the foot is wanting in both, the spreading head which covers a quadruple coil is easily recognizable as a type common in the third period of La Tène, and lasting down to the early Empire. Specimens found at Gurina were assigned by Dr. Tischler to the reign

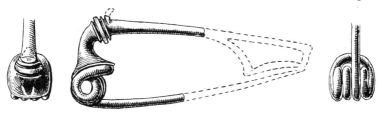

Fig. 138.—Bronze brooch, with details, Aylesford. ($\frac{1}{1}$)

of Claudius (A.D. 41–54), but from internal evidence it almost certainly arose at an earlier date, in direct imitation of the characteristic La Tène II type. The moulded collar, below which may be noticed the remains of a hooked projection supplied in the illustration (fig. 138), is evidently a reminiscence of the band which in the second century B.C. secured the tail of the brooch to the middle of the bow (fig. 51). As the foot did not survive in the Aylesford specimens, it is impossible to say whether it was entirely open or partially filled with crescents or step-work (as figs. 101, 165); but the restoration may be relied upon as more than probable.

Previous excavation on the same site had brought to light another grave, which contained the tankard here exhibited (fig. 139), and belonged to a group of burials to which the name 'family-circle' has been applied. The handles (fig. 140) suggest the use of another found at Hod Hill (fig. 146). Many graves were discovered from time to time, and were described as round pits 2–3 ft. deep containing two or three urns each, and grouped in irregular circles, perhaps containing contemporary burials of relatives. One such circle (fig. 141) had no mound or other external indication of the interments, which may therefore be assigned to the class known on the Continent as *Flachgräber* (surface-graves), as opposed to those covered by a mound or barrow (*Hügelgräber*).

Many of the urns discovered in this cemetery are exhibited in Case K, while others are preserved in the Ashmolean Museum at Oxford, together with a compact mass of eight bracelets of Kimmeridge shale, in the form of rings with circular section and an outside diameter of $3\frac{3}{8}$ in. Several small pits, 2 ft. in diameter at the mouth, and $1\frac{1}{2}$ ft. at the bottom, were found to contain charcoal and broken pottery like that used for the urns, but no burnt bones. These pits may well have been used as kilns for baking pottery made on the spot, and were quite distinct from

FIG. 139.—Bronze-mounted tankard, Aylesford. ($\frac{1}{4}$)

FIG. 140.—Handle of tankard, Aylesford. ($\frac{2}{3}$)

another circular pit 8 ft. in diameter and 12–13 ft. deep, which was entirely filled with animals' bones much decayed.

Some of the best urns from the site were found either in a large wooden tub or in the family-circle (fig. 141) to which it belonged. Only iron mounts remained, consisting of two iron ring-handles and part of a hoop with rivets; but these were sufficient to show that the diameter was about 40 in. Besides several cinerary urns, the vessel contained a quantity of flint flakes and scrapers, which had evidently been thrown in purposely, as was the case in other graves of the cemetery. The cinerary urns and associated vessels of pottery found in the graves were all made on the wheel, but varied considerably in shape, size, and colour like another group from the same county (fig. 142).

Though mica and minute grains of quartz may sometimes be detected in the Aylesford ware, the paste is mostly free from the grit and chalky particles that form so characteristic a feature of the Barrow pottery. The cinerary urns are of a light-brown substance, the surface being coloured with a black lustrous pigment formed probably of finely powdered charcoal, but now for the most part worn off. The vessels are also well baked and elegantly moulded, a few being of a pale brick colour resembling that of some Roman specimens. An important feature is the well-

FIG. 141.—Circle of interments, Aylesford.

turned pedestal on many of the cinerary urns, and it should be remarked that several urns found in Essex have the pedestal hollow as in the Marne district (fig. 64), while the Aylesford specimens have a solid and almost flat base, the same profile being retained. Raised ribs or cordons arranged horizontally are found on the majority, and are further defined by lateral grooves, dividing the body into zones that are sometimes decorated with linear ornament. The design in some cases consists of finely incised lines or comb-markings; in others a blunt point is drawn over the soft surface of the clay, producing a polished line.

Discovered in 1921, a British burial ground $3\frac{1}{2}$ miles south-west of Canterbury was excavated for the Society of Antiquaries, the pottery being repaired and subsequently presented by the Society to the Museum with the few other antiquities recovered from the urn-field, as such cremation cemeteries are generally called. The

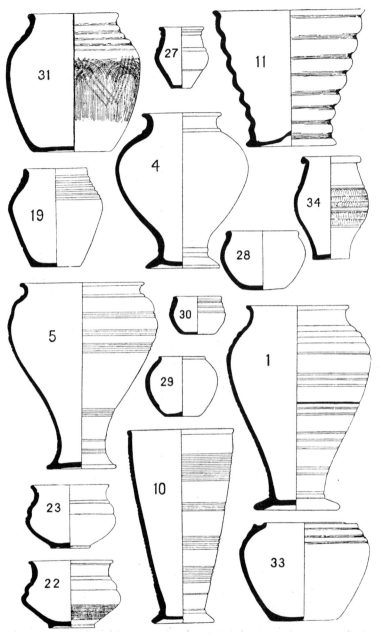

Fig. 142.—Pottery from Swarling, Kent (profile and section). ($\frac{1}{6}$)

site is above a chalk valley, on a gravel terrace behind Swarling
Manor. Mr. Bushe-Fox reported on the excavations which produced from 19 burials over 30 vessels more or less complete:
these are grouped in Case K, and the specimens selected for
illustration retain their type numbers (fig. 142). Two discovered
previously have been added by Dr. A. G. Ince. One of these
contained a bronze brooch of La Tène III, and the cemetery can
be assigned with confidence to the century 50 B.C.–A.D. 50. The
ware is uniform throughout, but the forms vary as much as at
Aylesford, and there are hardly two alike. The pedestal urns
of Swarling are less conical and have more flowing lines, and
though the broad ribs of Aylesford reappear, there is a lack of finely
modelled cordons in the new series. One tall urn recalls the

Fig. 143.—Pottery from Welwyn, Herts. $(\frac{1}{6})$

shale specimen in Case 21, but the general agreement with the
adjoining series in Case K is very striking, and the Aylesford
type is thus more firmly established as that connected with the
Cantii of Caesar's time (p. 11).

Though supervision was perfunctory, the discoveries at Welwyn
in 1906 have added a good deal to our knowledge of Britain in
Caesar's time; and except that the ironwork is here replaced by
wooden copies, most of the material is exhibited in standard-cases
H and J, as the gift of Mrs. Neall, daughter of Mr. G. E. Dering,
then owner of the site. The gravel hill, through which a new
road was being cut, probably contained several cremated burials
and a sacrificial outfit in two vaults as at Stanfordbury, Beds.
(Cambridge Museum). One of the two known burials was in a
hole $2\frac{1}{2}$ ft. deep, with a small pedestal urn (fig. 143, d) $7\frac{1}{2}$ in.
high, another narrower and taller, and the smaller *tazza* (e):
the other contained the taller of the two large pedestal urns
(13$\frac{3}{4}$ in. high), a reddish barrel-shaped vase (fig. 143, c), and
two bowls (a, f) holding the ashes. The ware is soft and
brown, thrown on the wheel and probably coated originally with
a black varnish which is better preserved on some of the smaller

pieces. Apart from the pottery, links with the Aylesford cemetery are the bronze *patella* of frying-pan shape, the two bronze jugs (found in fragments and now mounted on wooden models) and tankard with bronze handle, so that the approximate date is not in doubt; but there are new features—a pair of silver cups 4 in. high, evidently imported from Italy; the silver handles of a *kylix* or open cup on foot; three bronze escutcheons in the form of

masks, with moustache and hair in straight lines from back to front (with the cups in pl. XI); a bronze bowl of which the two odd drop-handles survive; three pairs of fire-dogs (andirons) measuring 42 in. between the uprights, and an iron frame (pl. XII), 42 in. high, which may have been a sacrificial table or altar, and was associated with five *amphorae* (fig. 144) or two-handled vessels 45-7 in. high, in which wine was imported from the Mediterranean countries. Fire-dogs were fairly common abroad in La Tène times, and elaborate specimens with fantastic boar's-head terminals and added horns are known from Denbighshire, Cambs., Essex, and Beds. The only parallels for the iron frame, however, seem to be those found near Arras in France and in Dépt. Marne.

The site of these discoveries is eight miles north-east of St. Albans, adjoining which is the Roman town of Verulamium; and here was probably the stockaded fort which served as the headquarters of Cassivellaunus in his resistance to Caesar in 54 B.C. The Catuvellauni over whom he ruled came originally from Châlons-sur-Marne, and their capital in Britain was transferred to Colchester by Cunobelin (Cymbeline); but as the Welwyn deposit appears to date from the reign of his grandfather (p. 170),

Fig. 144.—Amphora from Welwyn. $(\frac{1}{12})$

it was possibly connected with the royal house. In any case it supplies one interpretation of Caesar's statement that the Britons used imported bronze (vessels). This country is one of a limited number in which tin and copper naturally occur in considerable quantity, and both must have been worked here long before Caesar's time. He may, however, refer to coins which were struck abroad and imported into Britain for about a century before the British chieftains set up their own mints (p. 167).

Hod Hill is one of the hill-top camps which are now thought to date from the Early Iron Age. The summit of the hill is an irregular plateau more than 50 acres in extent, and the whole area is enclosed in a double line of ramparts with corresponding ditches (fig. 145). On the west and south the hill rises almost perpendicularly about 400 ft. above the river Stour, while the other sides are protected by earthworks, the inner ring rising about 60 ft. and the outer about 30 ft. above their respective fosses. A flanking entrance gave access on the north-east, and there are minor openings in the works which may not all be original. In the north-west angle was the later Roman encampment, which only needed fresh defences on the east and south. These, however, were of very moderate strength, consisting merely of a double ditch 5 ft. or 6 ft. deep, with a slightly raised platform running along the centre. The two entrances were protected by

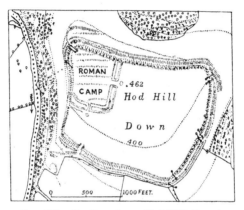

Fig. 145.—Earthworks on Hod Hill, Dorset.

slight breastworks, and the interior measured about 200 yards by 180 yards.

There are abundant traces of the native occupation of this stronghold, before the Romans under Vespasian reached this part of the country about A.D. 43. The entire area is thickly covered with artificial depressions marking the sites of hut-dwellings. Most of these are circular, with a diameter of 10-15 ft., and are often defined by a slight bank. Others have been noticed on the hill outside the enclosure, and some had evidently been cut through by the builders of the camp. The site was clearly occupied at a remote date, but the objects recovered in great quantity from the soil comprise few that can with certainty be referred to the period before the introduction of iron.

A selection from the series collected by the late Mr. Durden (of Blandford) is exhibited in Cases 22, 23. The enamelled studs clearly belong to the same culture as that revealed in the extensive

K

excavations of Bibracte (Mont Beuvray, Dépt. Saône-et-Loire), and though Hod Hill yields Roman antiquities of a date later than anything on the Gaulish site (p. 79), the relics show a remarkable similarity. Most of the British specimens from the site are mounted on one board, and include two handles (fig. 146) that may have belonged to a tankard (as fig. 139) or some larger vessel of that kind. The latest La Tène brooch is also represented, the catch-plate being solid. Later forms (as fig. 165) are evidently influenced by Roman models, and have a shield for the broad spiral spring at the head, and open-work catch-plate with step-pattern. A series of bone

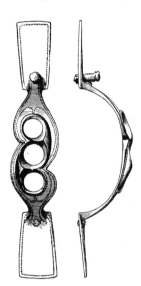

objects, including pins, bodkins, and pendants, should be compared with that from Spettisbury (below). A large quantity of iron tools, lance-heads, horse-furniture, and nails were collected on the site, both within and without the enclosure, but only a small selection can be exhibited. The Roman remains all belong to the first century of our era (Room of Roman Britain, Case B). The sword there shown with daggers and scabbard-mounts, scales of armour and cheek-pieces of helmets, shows the native adaptation of the Roman model, and should be compared with that from Cotterdale. A semi-circular chape on the same board, evidently belonging to the Roman short-sword, throws some light on the date of the Polden Hill hoard (p. 144).

In 1857, during the construction of the railway between Wimborne and Blandford, Dorset, an earthwork now called Crawford Castle was cut through, close to the village of Spettisbury. The

Fig. 146.—Bronze tankard-handle, Hod Hill. ($\frac{1}{2}$)

site for the stronghold had been well chosen, and the whole area surrounded by a moat. At the north corner a pit was discovered about 35 ft. long and 15 ft. wide, the depth varying from 4 ft. to 10 ft., and within had been placed irregularly eighty or ninety skeletons, among which were found several objects of interest. A sword-blade retained part of its iron scabbard, and is said to have resembled in form one from the Thames, originally in the collection of Lord Londesborough (the longest in Case 18). There were also some iron currency-bars of a type commonly found in the south of England, and two small bars of the same general form, but evidently intended to represent half the value of the commoner size (p. 165). A small bronze brooch, clearly derived from the

type of La Tène II, but with the spiral spring in T-form, has
an exterior chord (p. 51). The series also includes a cauldron
(fig. 147) of thin bronze with an iron rim, iron sickle-shaped or
'temple' keys (as at Tiefenau, Case 6), lance-heads (some with
split sockets), and the bronze chape and scabbard-edging of
a Roman short-sword, as at Hod Hill, the last affording an indication
of date.

Most of the bones were in a very friable condition, but two
skulls were recovered entire and submitted to Prof. Quekett.
One, that of a young man, had an index of 80 ; the other, probably

Fig. 147.—Bronze cauldron, Spettisbury, Dorset. ($\frac{1}{4}$)

belonging to a woman, was 77·2 : both may therefore be classed
as mesaticephalic.

The Glastonbury Lake-village has been fully published by
Messrs. Bulleid and Gray, and is of primary importance in the
history of pre-Roman Britain, giving as it does a vivid picture
of native life before the arts of Rome penetrated to the west of
England. The village is of the crannog type, the habitable area
of about $3\frac{1}{2}$ acres, originally in the middle of a mere, including
sixty or seventy dwellings which could be traced by slight mounds
in a meadow one mile north of the town. The excavation of the
site extended over several years, and a large collection of mis-
cellaneous relics was amassed, the absence of distinctively Roman
specimens being well established, though there is little to show
how long before our era the first settlement in this area had been
made. There was, however, time enough for 5 ft. of peat to
accumulate in some parts during the occupation. Vertical cuttings
through the mounds revealed a succession of well-defined strata of
clay, charcoal, ashes, and decayed wood ; but the most interesting

feature was the series of hearthstones within the hut-circle, showing successive occupation of the same spot, sometimes as many as four different floor-levels of compressed clay being noticed one above the other (fig. 148). The huts were mostly of circular plan, 18–35 ft. in diameter, the walls being constructed of wattle-and-daub, and supported by posts one foot apart which, with a centre-post, carried a thatched roof.   Each was surrounded by piles to increase the stability of the clay floor which rested on a regular layer of round timbers, laid close together on brushwood, as in the Swiss lake-dwellings.   These timbers extended under several hut-sites, and the whole village was surrounded by artificial ground strengthened with palisading and hurdles.

The absence of bronze implements shows that the earliest settlement dates from the Iron Age, and most of the brooches are of

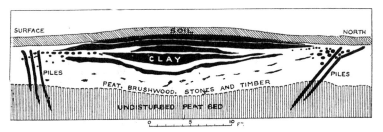

FIG. 148.—Vertical section of hut-circle, Glastonbury, Som.

La Tène III type, with open or solid catch-plate: a few specimens resembling in outline La Tène II type are compound (p. 37), and must be referred to the next stage. A few penannular specimens, common in the Roman period, were also discovered.   Several remarkable objects of wood have been recovered, and a restoration of a large bowl (fig. 149) cut from the solid and gracefully ornamented on the outside, is here exhibited. There was also the nave of a wheel, with axle-box 13 in. long, made on the lathe, which held twelve spokes 12 in. long: a ladder, 7 ft. long, and a dug-out canoe 18 ft. long, should also be mentioned, as well as some framework supposed to have formed part of a loom (as fig. 178). A great variety of bone combs, perhaps for pressing home the weft (p. 152), were also found.   The pottery is of exceptional interest, many pieces being ornamented with characteristic incised patterns quite distinct from the contemporary Aylesford series: some of it was hand-made, but many vessels were evidently made on the wheel.   Drawings are here reproduced (fig. 150) of a few restored urns in Glastonbury Museum.   A large number of well-made stone querns have been recovered, as at Hunsbury (p. 138); and the site has proved very prolific in pellets for slings, in shape like the Roman *glandes* of

lead but made of clay, which was either baked or unbaked. These
were, no doubt, used in the chase and not in warfare, as weapons
are extremely scarce here, only a few daggers having been found.
A bronze mirror, found with tweezers, antimony, and rouge,
marks the particular stage of civilization, and several crucibles
show that metallurgy was practised on the spot. The inhabitants

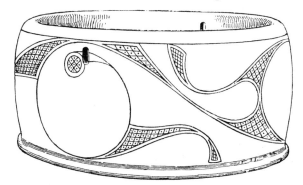

*Fig. 149.—Wooden bowl (restored), Glastonbury. ($\frac{1}{4}$)

*Fig. 150.—Pottery vessels, Glastonbury.

evidently grew wheat, and had sheep, cattle of the small breed
known as *Bos longifrons*, pigs, horses, and dogs ; but they also had
for food the stag, roe-deer, beaver, and otter of the district. The
absence of British coins (with a single exception) can be to
some extent explained by the presence of two iron currency-bars,
belonging to different denominations (p. 165).

The series from Hunsbury is hardly representative of the extensive finds on that site recorded by the late Sir Henry Dryden :
the bulk of the collection is in Northampton Museum. Here are
socketed spear-heads, knives, daggers, the grip of a sword, bone
cheek-pieces of bridle-bits, spindle-whorls, and a comb used in
weaving (as fig. 181) ; but mention must also be made of the more

characteristic objects that serve to date the occupation of this stronghold by the early Britons. Danes Camp, another name for Hunsbury, has as little historical foundation as Danes Graves in Yorkshire, and it was probably about 1,000 years before the arrival of the Norsemen that the site was inhabited: the ramparts may have been thrown up then, or at some earlier date in the Bronze period. The camp is about two miles south-west of North-ampton, and the ancient road called Banbury Lane passes within 300 yards of it on the north-west: the highest point is nearly 350 ft. above the sea. The enclosed area of four acres is approxi-mately oval in shape, the longest diameter being 560 ft. The defence consisted of one fosse only, 50 ft. to 65 ft. from edge to edge, the height of the scarp from the bottom of the fosse being about 15 ft., but originally more than 20 ft. Of the three entrances two are probably original, and suggest that the road that now skirts the camp on the south once passed through the centre. Ironstone diggings revealed over 300 circular refuse-pits scattered over the entire area, about 6 ft. deep and 5 ft. to 10 ft. in diameter. They were full of black mould, and contained the majority of relics. The most remarkable of these was an iron scabbard plated with bronze which is ornamented in characteristic style, the chape resembling that of the Bugthorpe example (fig. 124). The length is $30\frac{1}{4}$ in., while that of a plainer scabbard is $26\frac{3}{4}$ in., the sword belonging to the latter having a total length of 32 in. Of the brooches found, one very closely resembles fig. 95, but the foot is missing and the ornamentation of the bow is superior. Another is of La Tène III type (as fig. 52), and two others, though retaining traces of earlier forms, probably date from the early Empire. The pottery is instructive, with scroll designs incised in the unbaked clay, as at Yarnton (fig. 183): a remarkable feature is the rosette formed of dots which occurs within the bulbous loops, and also on a remarkable gilt brooch found at Tre'r Ceiri, Carnarvonshire, in association with Roman melon-shaped beads. Several pieces of horse-furniture, including bridle-bits of iron, were found, also spear-heads, bill-hooks, saws (as at Glastonbury), and loom-weights (as fig. 179), but there were no less than 150 quern-stones of grit in the form of truncated cones, well made with sockets for a single handle. One of the six skulls recovered had in it three holes drilled near the centre, suggesting a practice also exemplified in Gaul (fig. 61) at a somewhat earlier period. This was a male skull of mesaticephalic type (cephalic index 77), and closely resembled that of a young subject from the same site with an index of 76, while a third skull, of an adult male, must be classed as dolichocephalic (index 72).

The remarkable British antiquities from Stanwick (Cases 27, 28, 32-3) were discovered about 1844, and subsequently presented to the nation by Lord Prudhoe (fourth Duke of Northumberland).

Stanwick lies near the river Tees, about seven miles north of Richmond, in the North Riding of Yorkshire, and it was within formidable earthworks, which enclose about 800 acres, that the discovery was made, in a pit about 5 ft. from the surface. In the immediate neighbourhood were found large iron hoops that were doubtless tires of chariot-wheels such as have been found elsewhere in the county ; but it was remarked that neither Roman coins nor pottery were found within the earthworks, though they

Fig. 151.—Bronze terret for reins, Stanwick, N. R., Yorks. (⅔)

are only about a mile west of the great Roman road called Ermine Street. The camp is said to be the largest in England and may be attributed to the Brigantes.

The bulk of this find evidently consists of horse-trappings, those with lip-ornament (figs. 151, 152) being specially noticeable : some (as fig. 153) have circular sockets that were no doubt once filled with enamel. Other rings with open-work ornament exhibit both S

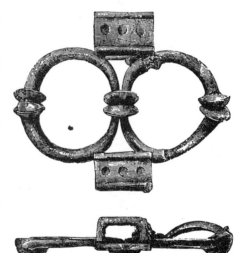

Fig. 152.—Double bronze ring, Stanwick. (½)

and C-scrolls (figs. 154, 155), also a device resembling a ribbon tied in a bow (fig. 156). Cheek-pieces for the bridle occur in more than one form, but are not so elaborate as the Polden Hill specimens (fig. 163), while the linch-pins (fig. 157) are here complete enough to show their original length and character ; some have a loop at the top, the others a ferrule-shape terminal of bronze, like those found at Westhall and Lisnacroghera (p. 160). As in the Homeric chariot, these may have been inserted vertically in the front end of the pole to hold the ring which supported the yoke ; and their decoration would there be seen to advantage. Indeed, the poet Pro-

FIG. 153.—Harness ring, Stanwick. ($\frac{1}{1}$)

FIG. 154.—Bronze open-work mount, Stanwick. ($\frac{2}{3}$)

FIG. 155.—Bronze open-work ring, Stanwick. ($\frac{2}{3}$)

FIG. 156.—Bronze open-work ring, Stanwick. ($\frac{1}{2}$)

pertius, who was born about 50 B.C., specially mentions the ornamented yokes of British chariots. Several bronze rings included in this find bear some resemblance to Somme Bionne examples (Case 16), and may, like them, have been fixed on the chariot-pole, to strengthen or adorn it. It should, however, be noted that linch-pins for chariot-wheels have been found in position, as at La Gorge Meillet (p. 55), where the central part of the stem was also of iron, as at Stanwick.

There are small metal bowls and embossed gold and bronze from Stanwick that show considerable technical skill, but as a representation of the human face the fragment here illustrated (fig. 158) must be pronounced a failure ; and that of a horse's head (fig. 159) though decorative is not more true to life. Further, there is a small fragment of shield-boss of the Polden Hill form, unornamented, but with a rivet in

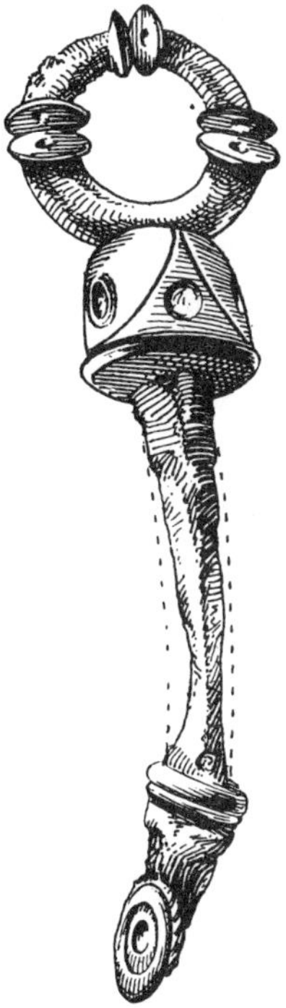

Fig. 157.— Bronze and iron linch-pin, Stanwick. ($\frac{1}{2}$)

Fig. 158.—Bronze embossed with mask, Stanwick. ($\frac{2}{3}$)

position on the edge ; and the fragments of chain-mail evidently belonged to a warrior's cuirass.

An interesting suggestion as to the use of certain lyre-shaped ornaments (fig. 160) was made by Déchelette. Two specimens had been placed in the grave of a soldier at Chassenard, Dépt. Allier, and on the perfect one there remained a patch of chain-mail, attached by a stud at the base. This was a burial after cremation, and the calcined bones were placed in a *dolium* of grey ware, the date being determined from various considerations as about

A. D. 40. Among other objects in the grave were a rectangular buckle-plate in relief resembling some of silver from Hod Hill (Case 23), a hinged collar of flat section, and an iron mask which had evidently served as the vizor of a helmet (cf. the Ribchester helmet in Room of Roman Britain). The Chassenard specimen had a camail of chain-mail attached, and certain pieces of mail

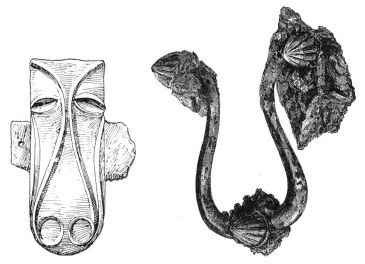

FIG. 159.—Bronze embossed with horse's head, Stanwick. ($\frac{1}{2}$)

FIG. 160.—Mount of chain-mail cuirass, Stanwick. ($\frac{1}{1}$)

FIG. 161.—Bronze band with rosettes, Stanwick. ($\frac{1}{1}$)

with rosettes (as fig. 161) were found at Stanwick. Livy records that in the year 293 B.C. the consul, Papirius Cursor, bestowed the decoration called the *corniculum* on his cavalry at Aquilonia, and it is clear from Suetonius that it was still in use towards the end of the Republic, and this may be an example ; but there is no literary evidence as to the precise manner in which it was worn. Several monuments show that in Imperial times torcs and *phalerae* were worn on the cuirass ; and it is fairly certain that the Chassenard burial is that of a Roman legionary of the time of Caligula.

Perhaps the finest series of Early-British antiquities in existence was discovered in 1800 near the top of the Polden Hills, above Edington, Somerset (Cases 29, 30, 33).   They were scattered by the plough, but had evidently been deposited together in a round hole about the size of a bushel measure, the bottom having been lined with burnt clay.   No less than fourteen bronze bridle-bits (fig. 162) of excellent work were included in this hoard, some being almost identical with a pair from Lanaber, Merionethshire (Case 29): they varied in size, but all were of the same style, some having circular sockets, which were filled with enamel, as at Stanwick. Some striking specimens of enamel decoration were also found,

FIG. 162.—Bronze bridle-bit, Polden Hill, Som. ($\frac{1}{2}$)

in which the red retains much of its brilliancy, though in places turned green by oxidation.   In one case the bronze is still of a golden colour, while in the best example (plate VIII, no. 3) the ground has been blackened, the surface being exceptionally lustrous.   There are five enamelled cheek-pieces (fig. 163) for the bridle, and two iron specimens, as well as an engraved and embossed bronze that may have been a horse's frontal, like one from Pompeii. An iron torc, bound spirally with bronze wire, also calls for remark, as iron specimens are extremely rare in this country (p. 149) ; and two stout armlets of bronze with overlapping ends are not unlike specimens found in the North of Europe during the earliest Teutonic period : one in the Morel collection (Case 14) bears a basket-shaped pendant.   It is significant also that the three bronze shield-bosses from Polden Hill, of which one is illustrated (fig. 164), are allied to those from Thorsbjerg Moss, Flensborg (p. 82).

The semicircular sword-chape of bronze has a Roman look (specimen with Hod Hill sword and daggers in Room of Roman Britain, Case B), and the three brooches found can also be matched in the Roman series. The best preserved has a cylindrical cover for the spiral spring at the head, and an open-work foot with a characteristic step-pattern (fig. 165). Lastly, a peculiar bronze with conical centre, from which radiate three (or four) stems each ending in a ring (fig. 166), seems to be derived from a pattern common in Italy, in which the centre consists of tapering spikes separated from each other by equal spaces, and a loop on two sides (fig. 167). Italian specimens with the spikes coalescing are extant, and the grooves on the Polden Hill example may represent the original interstices. These bronzes are generally, but incorrectly, termed 'bow-pullers': they are more likely 'bridle-spurs', to be attached to the head-stall of a horse and driven into the side of the nose by pulling the rein; and some have been found with iron chains passing through the loops and under the cone. The smaller size of the British example may be due to its manufacture for a pony, and the principle is seen on a bit in Case 65 (*Anglo-Saxon Guide*, fig. 225).

Fig. 163.— Enamelled cheek-piece of bridle, Polden Hill. ($\frac{3}{4}$)

An important series of bronzes was discovered in 1854 in draining a field at Westhall, a small village about three miles north-east of Halesworth, Suffolk. The soil is here a stiff clay, but a space of about two acres had, after ploughing, a much darker appearance than the rest. At a depth between $1\frac{1}{2}$ and 3 ft. the ground had been blackened by fire, and contained much charcoal, as well as pottery fragments in great variety, but no complete vessels could be found. A solitary piece of a plain 'Samian' patera was turned up, but not in immediate association with the bronzes, which had been packed in a thin bronze vessel in the centre of the blackened area. The restored design of some bronze fragments consists of an embossed cruciform pattern with palm-branches between the arms and is discussed below (p. 163). Several enamelled horse-trappings (probably 'terrets' for the reins) from this site are exceptionally fine, and some still retain the vivid red of the enamel. Six bronze terminals, with remains of iron inside, were probably the heads of linch-pins, like those at Stanwick (fig. 157). The use of a number of polished pebbles

from this site is unexplained, but a clue to the date is afforded by
a bronze pear-shaped lamp of Roman work, with a crescent above

FIG. 164.—Embossed shield-boss, Polden Hill. $(\frac{1}{3})$

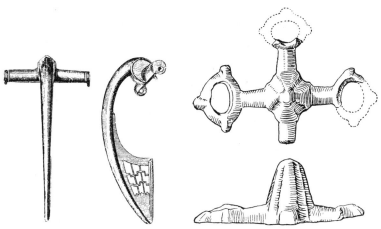

FIG. 165. Bronze brooch, Polden
Hill. $(\frac{1}{2})$

FIG. 166.—' Bridle-spur ', Polden Hill
(top and side views). $(\frac{2}{3})$

the ring handle, as well as by a bronze coin of Faustina the Elder (A.D. 138-41). It is interesting to find here a small bronze disc embossed with an animal form (fig. 168) closely related to those on the Aylesford bucket below, and on Gaulish coins of the period.

Enamelled bridle-bits have been already mentioned (p. 103): others not so well preserved as that from Rise are in Case 29 with a group of terrets, enamelled or plain, of various patterns;

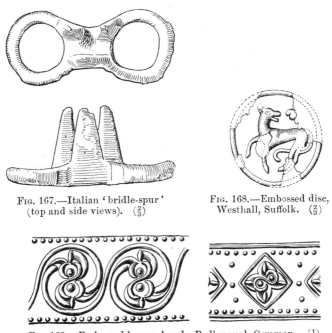

Fig. 167.—Italian 'bridle-spur' (top and side views). ($\frac{2}{3}$)

Fig. 168.—Embossed disc, Westhall, Suffolk. ($\frac{2}{3}$)

Fig. 169.—Embossed bronze bands, Rodborough Common. ($\frac{1}{2}$)

and the British specimen from the Fayùm in Case 8 should not be forgotten (p. 87). It was perhaps taken there by a Roman soldier who had served in Britain, and another has recently been found at Eauze, Dépt. du Gers, in S. France. A remarkable series of bronze strips with embossed designs (fig. 169) in Case 30 come from Rodborough Common, near Stroud, Gloucs., but their application is not apparent. A comparatively early date is indicated for three bronze discs from the Thames (fig. 170), resembling in style those from Somme Bionne (plate IV); and all have holes at the top for suspension (perhaps a later adaptation). Three mysterious bronze castings in Case 18 are generally called hubs or axle-ends: others are in Manchester, Leicester, and Taunton Museums, and Brentford Public Library. The specimen illustrated (fig. 171) is peculiar in having a bar across the neck and an ornamental disc (like some in Case 23) with a long pin loose in one of the openings. The other two are from the Thames at Goring and Burwell Fen, Cambs.

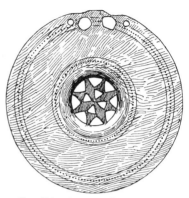

The boar has been already mentioned in connexion with the Witham shield, which once had a bronze badge of that animal affixed to the front by rivets; and a series of bronze figures in the round are here shown from Hounslow. They were found in the same field as some implements of the Bronze Age, but not in association, and include three boars (fig. 172) and two other nondescript animals, one with a loop for

FIG. 170.—Open-work bronze disc, Thames at Hammersmith. ($\frac{2}{3}$)

suspension: it is possible that some, like that from Guilden Morden, were crests of helmets. The boar frequently occurs on British and Gaulish coins of the period, and examples have been found as far off as Gurina (p. 79) and Transylvania. In the same field at Hounslow

FIG. 171.—'Axle-end' (with top view and section), Thames at Putney. ($\frac{1}{3}$)

was found the bronze wheel (fig. 172) with four spokes and a diameter of $1\frac{1}{2}$ in. like another from Colchester. A wheel of the same character belongs to the Stanwick find, but has a rectangular loop at the back; and all may have been connected with sun-worship. It was more probably as a religious symbol than as a survival of the chariot-wheel (p. 167), or a form of currency, that the wheel occurs on the coinage of Gaul and Britain (plate XIII, nos. 5, 13). There are some Gaulish wheels in Case 13.

The bronze statuette (fig. 173) found at the base of the cliffs at Aust-on-Severn is of exceptional interest. It represents a female figure, probably a goddess, with a peculiar crescent-shaped head-dress seen on the Spanish example (fig. 73) to which it bears

FIG 172.—Bronze wheel and boars, Hounslow, Middlesex. $(\frac{2}{3})$

a close resemblance in form and style. In one of the eye sockets remains a glass bead; and sockets at the ears were probably filled in the same way. The oxidation has given a reddish tinge to some parts of the surface, and there are signs that iron pins, for supporting the figure on a plinth, have been inserted in the feet. The second statuette from Spain shows still ruder manufacture, but the features are executed in the same style; and it is interesting to note that among other figures found at Aust was one of a male divinity, bearing the ram's horns usually associated with Jupiter Ammon. It is quite conceivable that the deposit to which the two British specimens belonged was made by Phoenician traders to our shores; but the find is now dispersed, and no complete record of the discovery exists.

FIG. 173.—Bronze statuette, Aust-on-Severn. $(\frac{1}{2})$

Besides the specimens illustrated (fig. 174), there are in the collection two other spoon-shaped bronzes from London: one from the Thames, the other from Brick Hill Lane, Upper Thames Street. Nineteen are known from the British Isles, and they are generally found in pairs, one having a cross incised in the bowl, and the other a hole pierced near one edge (always the same). A pair came from a burial at Deal, one on either side of the skull; and another pair has recently been published from a grave near Burnmouth, Berwickshire, where an iron knife and bones of a young pig also accompanied a man's skeleton. Two from Pogny, Dépt. Marne, were found in a woman's grave, one quite plain, the other pierced in the centre of the incised cross. These mysterious objects have been found in England, Wales, Scotland, and Ireland, with various designs on the handle, but all of the same general shape and size. If for ceremonial use, they may be connected with the Druidic cult, as there was no other authority in the Early Iron Age common to all four countries and to France.

Further discoveries of torcs in association with datable objects must be made in the British Isles before a definite chronological

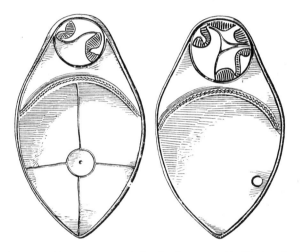

Fig. 174.—Pair of bronze 'spoons', Crosby Ravensworth, Westmorland. (½)

sequence can be formulated; but the affinities of those in the collection and a few others may be briefly indicated. Two bronze terminals from Colchester belonged to a specimen of Gaulish type (fig. 60, no. 10), no doubt an importation: part of a gilt torc from Slay Hill Saltings on the Medway near Upchurch (Case D, Room of Roman Britain) seems to be a native copy of the same type, and was found with Roman finger-rings, a coin of Aurelius (161–80), and a plain silver collar which agrees well with that found in the Polden Hill hoard, except that the latter is wound round with bronze wire. Perhaps an earlier native type is that exemplified at Rudbaxton, Pembrokeshire, where two complete iron rings were found with a model hand of the same metal, probably of a votive character. Another iron torc was found on the neck of a skeleton at Arras, and others appear to have been found at Ham Hill, Somerset, and Dorchester, Dorset.   Herodian, about A.D. 238, stated that the northern tribes of Britain adorned their flanks and

Fig. 175.—Portions of gold torc (with details), Clevedon, Som.   ($\frac{2}{3}$)

Fig. 176.—Bronze collar, Isle of Portland, Dorset.   ($\frac{1}{2}$)

necks with iron, considering it an ornament and sign of wealth, as other barbarians consider gold.

The fragments of a remarkable gold torc from Somerset (fig. 175) are a late British development of a Gaulish prototype (fig. 60, no. 1).

The terminals are hollow, and seem out of proportion to the hoop of three strands; while the basket-work design included in the ornamentation is suggestive of the bronze mirrors (figs. 132, 133) and other objects (fig. 124) found in south Britain.

There is another series, made on different lines, of which an early specimen is a bronze penannular collar from Greenhill, Weymouth, its flat terminals set with small glass pastes. Similar settings are found on that from Trenoweth, Cornwall, which has the ring complete and is lined with lead; while a later development seems to be the hinged collar (fig. 176) found in a grave with a 'Samian' bowl in the Isle of Portland. This is practically identical with one from Stitchel, Roxburghshire, and both can hardly be earlier than A. D. 100.

About the same date are a number of bronze clasps (serving the purpose of buttons) found generally on military sites in Britain, as Colchester, York (fig. 177), Lincoln, and New-

Colchester.　　　　York.

Fig. 177.—Bronze clasps (front and side views.) ($\frac{2}{3}$)

stead (Melrose). Some have quite plain discs, others a pointed oval plate moulded in the British style, but it was not a purely native type as examples are published from the Saalburg near Homburg.

Spindle-whorls are among the commonest objects belonging to the Early Iron Age in this and other countries, though in the North of Europe they are seldom found in association with remains of the Bronze period. This is one of several indications that the arts of civilization spread but slowly from the great centres of European culture in the Mediterranean. Before being woven into cloth, thread must be spun from wool, flax, or other fibrous material which is placed on a distaff. This is seen leaning against the loom in the illustration (fig. 178) and from it hangs by a thread the spindle, which consists of a wooden rod about 9 in. long, rounded and tapering towards the ends. At the top is a notch in which the yarn is secured during the operation of spinning, and somewhat below the middle is the whorl, a perforated disc of stone or other heavy substance to give momentum and steadiness to the spindle when it is rotated by the spinner. The process was subsequently superseded by the spinning-wheel, but in early times the distaff was held under the left arm of the operator, the spindle twirled between the fingers of the right hand, and the fibre drawn from the distaff in a uniform strand between the fingers of both hands, being twisted at the same time into yarn. Before the spindle touches the ground, the thread is wound round it and caught in the notch ; and when, after a number of such lengths have been wound, the spindle is full, it is laid aside for the weaver and replaced by another. The spindle being generally of wood is comparatively scarce, but large numbers of whorls have been found on most ancient sites and are some-times elaborately orna-mented. Examples from Glastonbury are shown in Case 22. Loom-weights of baked clay or stone were hung on the ends of the warp-threads to provide the necessary tension (fig. 178). The triangular pattern (fig. 179), with two or three per-forations across the corners, is not uncommon in England, but many are four-sided, taper-ing towards the top (fig. 180).

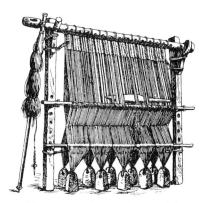

*Fig. 178.—Primitive loom, with weights, distaff, and spindle.

The bone hand-comb, perhaps used for beating in the weft on the loom, is also a common relic on Early British sites, and is well represented in the collection. Two of the usual types are illus-trated (fig. 181), with oblong and circular heads respectively : the

Fig. 179.—Clay loom-weight, Brooke, Norfolk. ($\frac{1}{6}$)

Fig. 180.—Clay loom-weight, Lakenheath, Suffolk. ($\frac{1}{6}$)

ends are sometimes pointed or rounded off without expansion, and the ornamentation is of a primitive description consisting of lines or groups of ring-and-dot pattern and plain double lines arranged in zigzags or lozenges. An exceptionally long specimen ($8\frac{1}{2}$ in.)

is shown from Glastonbury, and one found in a weem (earth-house) near Kirkwall, Orkney, has the teeth of unequal lengths.

Apart from the Aylesford, Swarling, and Welwyn series in the standard cases, pottery is exhibited in Cases 20, 21. Beside the pedestal urns (probably cineraries) from Kent, Arlesey (Beds.), and Hitchin (Herts.), there are certain forms that seem to have been purely domestic ; and in certain districts of south Britain a well-defined type is fairly common. The body is more or less ovate, with rounded shoulder and slight rim, also a pair of stout ring handles,

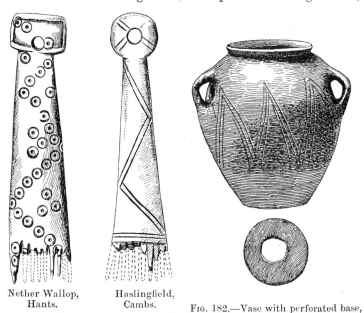

Nether Wallop,   Haslingfield,
Hants.   Cambs.   FIG. 182.—Vase with perforated base,
FIG. 181.—Bone weaving-combs. ($\frac{1}{2}$)   Fordingbridge, Hants. ($\frac{1}{4}$)

which either stand out boldly from the shoulder or are placed over indentations which allow a passage for the finger. This is the countersunk handle which has a long history abroad, but seems to be confined to the Early Iron Age in Britain (fig. 182). Several examples from Dorset are exhibited. The surface is smooth and the paste fairly homogeneous, with a brownish-black surface, but most of the pottery was handmade, and not produced on the potter's wheel. A peculiar feature, to be observed on several pieces in the collection, is the perforation of the base, and it has been plausibly suggested that such vessels were used for draining honeycomb, the honey passing out through one or more holes into another vessel below. Examples of this type have been found in

Hants (fig. 182), Dorset, Wilts., and Kent (Ramsgate) ; and can be readily distinguished from more advanced specimens that betray contact with Roman civilization.

Except at Glastonbury (fig. 150) free-hand decoration is rare ; and it is worth while illustrating two fragments (fig. 183) which show varieties of the scroll pattern, incised or stamped.

Four of the series here illustrated from Hitchin (fig. 184) were presented by Mr. Francis Ransom, with several well-preserved vases

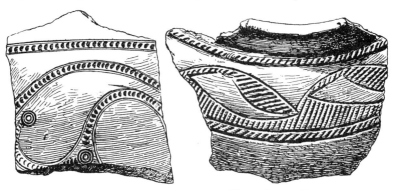

Yarnton, Oxon.   Kent's Cavern, Torquay.

Fig. 183.—Ornamented fragments of pottery. ($\frac{1}{2}$)

Fig. 184.—Early British pottery, Hitchin, Herts. ($\frac{1}{10}$)

from Grove Mill near that town, and from Arlesey, Beds. There were no surface indications of burials at Hitchin, but as calcined bones were mixed with the earth, the pottery may be explained without hesitation as burial deposits, presumably of the Catuvellauni. Midway between Arlesey and Bedford lies Old Warden, where the imperfect cordoned vase of Kimmeridge shale was found ; the lower part is restored after others associated with it and now in Cambridge Museum.

Fragments found at Deal and given by Mr. Hazzledine Warren belonged to two urns with interesting decoration reminiscent of the Marne (Case G). One had a tall vertical neck, and was incised with fret and other geometrical patterns at intervals ; the other was biconical, and had chevrons and groups of sloping lines incised in three zones above the shoulder. Being found on the Kentish coast, they may well have been brought over from France in the early days of La Tène. The carinated bowl with incurved sides from Kelvedon, Essex, is dated by the brooch found with it (La Tène III) ; and allied forms of the bowl are exhibited from Ashwell and Welwyn, Herts. One large urn, other smaller vessels, and several fragments, some decorated, in Case 20 come from an Early Iron Age site at Wisley, Surrey, previously occupied by Neolithic man, the two series of pit-dwellings being easily distinguishable. One specimen is illustrated (fig. 185) to show the decoration of the lip and the angular shoulder, but it is at present uncertain to what century or to what tribe this ware belonged.

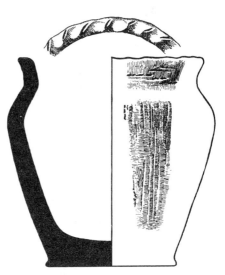

FIG. 185.—Vase with ornamented lip, Wisley, Surrey. ($\frac{1}{2}$)

The series from North Britain is small, but comprises certain objects of exceptional interest and value. The pair of enamelled bronzes, in the form of armlets, from Pitkelloney, near Drummond Castle, Perthshire, may be regarded as typical of a group found (with a single exception from Ireland) on what is now Scottish soil. A considerable number exist, nearly all being from beyond the Firth of Forth, and they have been divided into two classes, according as the bands of which they are composed run horizontally, or in a spiral curve ending abruptly (as fig. 186). The two exhibited weigh 3 lb. 13$\frac{1}{2}$ oz. (1·87 kilog.) and 3 lb. 9$\frac{3}{4}$ oz. (1·82 kilog.) respectively, with an internal diameter of 4$\frac{1}{2}$ in., and are much too heavy and unwieldy to have been worn habitually on the upper arm ; but as objects of parade they would have served as admirable examples of Early British art. The decoration has no early features (such as the remnants of the palmette seen on the Witham shield), but consists of graceful curves in relief with oblique projections at intervals somewhat resembling the lip pattern (p. 98) which is seen on either side of the point of junction. The oval space within the ring-ends is filled with red and yellow enamels in cruciform and quatrefoil patterns, and the bronze plate on which the enamels are set rests on an iron plate (seen from the back) and is kept in position by bronze bands passing along the grooves between the heavier coils. These smaller bands, which have a casing moulded to imitate coiled wire, are therefore constructional in the present instance, but in time become a mere ornamental feature. How long this evolution occupied is at present uncertain, but, according to all available evidence, the yellow enamel shows that these two specimens belong at the earliest to the Roman period, and may possibly be

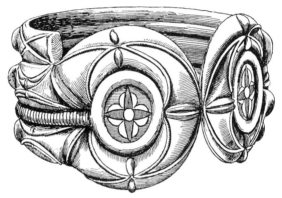

FIG. 186.—Enamelled bronze, Drummond Castle, Perthshire. ($\frac{1}{2}$)

some centuries later than the conquest under Claudius. Examples have been found with a skillet of pure Italian work of the first or second century at Stanhope, Peeblesshire, and analysis shows that one Aberdeenshire specimen contained three times as much zinc as tin, the copper amounting to 88 per cent. Zinc first appears in Roman alloys, at the beginning of the Christian era.

It would be hard to prove that the enamelled bronzes found in Scotland are earlier than the first century of our era; and it is probable that British art in Scotland began to flourish during the Roman occupation of the southern half of our island. Brooches of early La Tène type are comparatively numerous in England (p. 94), but true examples, with bilateral spring and open foot, have not been found in Scotland, though a few derivative forms and even Italian specimens are exhibited at Edinburgh: of the latter, two localities are known. Remoteness from the Continent would at that time account for a tardy adoption of artistic motives, as well as for their retention after new models had been introduced

into more favoured regions. It was in the year A. D. 80 that
Agricola first led a Roman army across the border and established
between the Firths of Forth and Clyde a line of forts that were

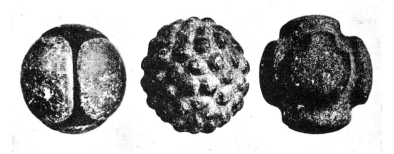

| Stanwix,
Cumberland. | Novar House,
Cromarty Firth. | Ballymena,
co. Antrim. |

Fig. 187.—Ornamented stone balls. (½)

merged in the Antonine wall about the middle of the second
century. But the Caledonians asserted their independence from
time to time, and the Roman occupation of the Lowlands was
neither so complete
nor so prolonged as
that of southern
Britain, while the
Highlands were prac-
tically untouched by
the Romans. Tacitus
regarded the red hair
and large limbs of
the Caledonians as a
proof of their German
origin ; but the racial
question has been dis-
cussed above (p. 10).
Various remains from
Scotland here ex-
hibited (Case 24) call
for some remark. The
series of ornamented
stone balls practi-
cally confined to that

Fig. 188.—Beaded collar, Lochar Moss,
Dumfriesshire. (⅓)

country is well represented, and two from the North are illustrated
(fig. 187) with the solitary one found in Ireland. All these are of

stone (only one is known of bronze), and various qualities were used for the purpose, which is still obscure ; and so far no proof of their date has been discovered, but from the style of certain specimens, the group probably belongs to the early centuries of our era.

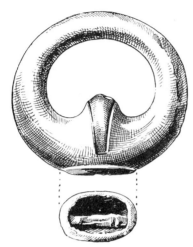

FIG. 189.—Bronze terret (with base view), Inverury, Aberdeenshire. ($\frac{2}{3}$)

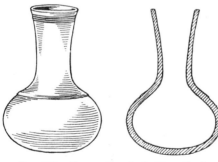

FIG. 190.—Bronze ferrule (with section), Inverury. ($\frac{2}{3}$)

The peculiar melon-shaped beads of turquoise-coloured glass, common on Roman sites in Britain and elsewhere, perhaps suggested the form of the beads forming the back portion of the remarkable bronze collar (fig. 188) from Lochar Moss. It was found inside a small bronze bowl of excellent workmanship, and has a rigid front ornamented with a running scroll of peculiar form. This, to all appearance, is a development of the pattern seen on the Bapchild 'terret' described by Sir Hercules Read, and appears to be ultimately derived from a classical source (p. 20). Similar beads, apparently belonging to a collar of this form, were found at Hyndford Crannog, Lanarkshire, and a similar collar, with beads of another pattern, has been found near Rochdale.

A bronze terret (p. 189) and ferrule of a spear (fig. 190) were found at Inverury, Aberdeenshire, with four jet balls which are pierced and were probably the heads of iron hair-pins: amber specimens with bronze shafts have been found in Switzerland and appear to have radiated from a leather band placed on top of the head.

Ferrules of this type, resembling a door-handle, have also been found in England (Rushall Down, Wilts.) and Ireland (Case 24); and a possible prototype accompanied bronze spear-heads at Fulbourn, Cambs. Xiphilinus, who epitomized the history of Dio Cassius, in speaking of the Caledonians in the time of Severus (3rd century A. D.), states that they carried a shield and short spear with bronze ferrule which when shaken made a noise to terrify their enemies.

An iron sword from the Shannon near Athlone is the only object referable to the Hallstatt period at present known in Ireland ; but the period of La Tène is better represented, at least in its later stages (after 300 B. C.). The sculptured standing-stones of Turoe, co. Galway (of which a cast adjoins Case K), Castle Strange (co. Roscommon), and Mullaghmast (co. Kildare), date from La Tène II or III, and the first has been compared with the Kermaria stone (Pont l'Abbé, Finistère) : the parallel recalls the more ancient connexion between the chambered barrows of New Grange near Drogheda and Gavr'inis in the adjoining department of Morbihan. Another series of glass beads, with other patterns not confined to Ireland, may be seen in the Glass and Ceramic Gallery, but no precise date or sequence has yet been determined for them. They are generally referred to the Early Iron Age, though the late Mr. E. C. R. Armstrong published evidence of association with Viking remains in Dublin Museum from Island Bridge, Kilmainham, co. Dublin : in any case they were probably made in Egypt or some other Mediterranean country (p. 120). The three specimens illustrated (fig. 131, nos. 4–6) are of dark-blue glass, and spiral threads with light markings are applied to the surface in a variety of patterns. Others, of spindle-whorl form, are often blotched with colours, and another type has knobs as well as spiral coils ; while the dumb-bell and Roman melon shapes also occur.

There are at Dublin two Italian brooches of early types (as fig. 40, nos. IId, IIe), but, as generally in the British Isles, there is no definite information about them, and some may have been brought from Italy in recent times. Other brooches known to have been found in Ireland are evidently derived from La Tène models, and are sometimes of remarkable elegance (fig. 191), but here again there is a considerable deviation from the original. This of course does not necessarily imply any considerable interval of time, but everything points to a protracted development of other ornamental objects. The evolution of the hand-type of pin—so called from the resemblance of its head to the front aspect of a closed hand—has been already traced (p. 97), and though it seems to have originated in the south of Britain, its latest stages are almost confined to Ireland, Scotland, and the north of England (Moresby, Cumberland), the specimen from Sussex (Case 54) being probably an importation from Ireland.

The crannog or lake-dwelling at Lisnacroghera, near Brough-shane, co. Antrim, is well known, and has proved to be rich in antiquities, of which the finest is the en-graved bronze scabbard (fig. 192) here exhibited with other remains from the site. Little notice was taken of the pile-structure that existed where the relics were found, but it seems to have resembled that at Glaston-bury (fig. 148). Weapons were comparatively plentiful, as many as four swords being recovered, mostly in a damaged condition; the scabbard-chapes were of the common Irish type (specimens in Case 19, and fig. 192), derived from La Tène forms (fig. 56, no. 3) but easily distinguishable as a local

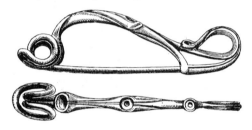

FIG. 191.—Bronze brooch, Clogher, co. Tyrone. ($\frac{2}{3}$)

adaptation. The designs engraved on the bronze scabbards are of the highest merit, but have no early features, one having the basket-pattern seen on the mirror from St. Keverne (fig. 132); and the cup-shaped hollows may have been originally filled with enamel as a ring pin-head undoubtedly was. The sword has a curved guard, as in La Tène II, corresponding to the mouth of the scabbard. The bronze ferrules were apparently the heads of iron linch-pins, and the same pattern was found at Harray broch, Orkney. An iron adze and sickle (as from La Tène, Case 6) should be noticed; and it may be added that swastika and fret designs were found on bronze mountings in the crannog.

A facetted stone ball (fig. 187) from Ballymena, co. Antrim, has been already

FIG. 192.—Scabbard, Lisnacroghera bog, Skerry, co. Antrim. ($\frac{1}{4}$)

referred to as a Scottish type, and a general resemblance between Irish bronze bowls and that from Lochar Moss should be noticed. The pair of stout horns, which may have been enamelled, probably served some ornamental purpose on a chariot, as the nearest parallel was found in the grave of a charioteer at Arras, Yorks., more than a century ago.

The bronze disc (fig. 193), with sunk centre and ornament in relief, is a fine specimen of its class, of which six are preserved at

Fig. 193.—Bronze disc with well, Ireland. ($\frac{1}{4}$).

Dublin, all presenting the same essential features. Their use is problematical, but it is conceivable that they were set on a turf mound or other pedestal for burning incense, the cup-shaped hollow suggesting the top of a Roman altar. The pair of bronze spur-shaped objects found near Galway with a bridle-bit seem to have formed part of a horse's equipment, but are shown, by the wear of similar examples from Ireland, to have been suspended, and not worn upright over the horse's head. One is published from co. Roscommon, attached by small chains to a bridle-bit; but the best specimen (fig. 194) came from the Tower of London Armoury without a history, and has fixed and movable attachments for straps, and an open terminal with scroll-work. Its extreme dimensions are 11 in. × 7½ in., and it should be remarked that only one branch of the fork is ornamented, as though to be seen only from one side. Several bridle-bits are shown of a type common in Ireland, the two larger limbs of the bit being arched and expanding outwards beyond the junction with the rings. There is a good specimen of this type from co. Wicklow, but besides this the more usual pattern, common in Britain, was also used in Ireland.

Another link with Britain is the supposed water-clock from Lisnacroghera bog, co. Antrim (fig. 195), which is the best preserved of all and is exhibited with others in Case 31.

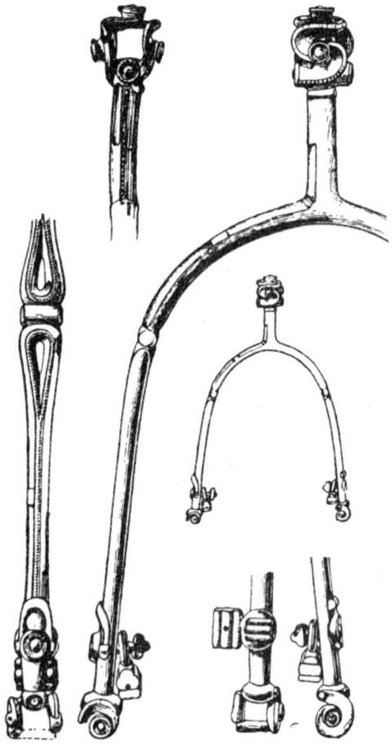

Local differences in the Early Iron Age civilization of the British Isles are plainly discernible and may reflect the ethnology of the period ; but there is one group of objects common to England and Ireland which may have a bearing on one of the most controversial points in our history. The first hint was given in 1906 by the large cauldron-like vessel hung in Case 31 (like fig. 196), from Baschurch, Shropshire, where it was found in swampy ground beside a causeway leading to a circular earthwork called the Berth, originally in a large mere, which is now reduced to a pool of seven acres. The vessel is nearly complete, but anchor - shaped marks on the side suggest that it originally had one or two arched handles. What remains weighs nearly 3½ lb., and about 6 oz. of metal is missing, apart from the handle and attachments, the maximum diameter being 17¾ in. In the centre of the base is a neatly drilled circular hole ⅕ in. in diameter, which recalls much smaller bowls used till recently in India and Ceylon for measuring time by placing them on the surface of water in a larger vessel, and allowing the water to percolate through the aperture. In a definite time the vessel sinks and is then replaced on the surface by an attendant, who announces the lapse of a time-unit by beating a gong or by some other sound-signal. About thirty bronze vessels so pierced have since been recognized in the British Isles ; but as the metal is thin and easily

FIG. 194.—Spur-shaped bronze (with enlarged details), Ireland. (⅑ and ⅓).

rendered useless for such a delicate operation as measuring time, they often had the perforation plugged, and served more ordinary purposes. The set found packed in straw at Wotton, Surrey, is exhibited with others, and consists of a bronze 'frying-pan' originally with wooden handle (probably the gong), and nine bowls, two of which are perforated and three plugged. The only

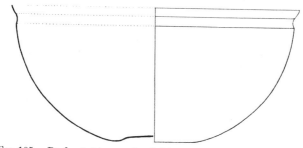

Fig. 195.—Perforated bronze bowl, Lisnacroghera bog, Antrim. ($\frac{1}{2}$)

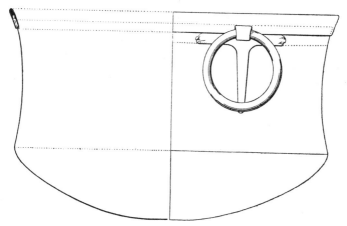

Fig. 196.—Bronze vessel with iron handle, Wotton, Surrey. ($\frac{1}{6}$)

decorated bowl (fig. 197) is embossed with a radiating pattern recalling the fragments in the Westhall hoard (p. 144), which also contained a flat bar that may have served as a beater for the gong, a similar outfit having been found at Sturmere, Essex, in 1807. The four largest vessels from Wotton are too much damaged to be weighed, but the others (when compensated for missing portions) are found to weigh 11, $16\frac{1}{2}$, 21, $27\frac{1}{4}$, and $33\frac{1}{4}$ oz. almost exactly in the proportion of 1, $1\frac{1}{2}$, 2, $2\frac{1}{2}$, and 3. The unit weight is represented by the ornamented bowl, and agrees with a bronze weight marked I found with British enamelled bronze at Neath, Glamorganshire (National Museum of Wales at Cardiff) ; and this unit of 4,770 grains = 309 grammes (about 11 oz. Av.) seems to apply equally well to the primitive iron currency of the Britons mentioned (and probably seen) by Caesar in 54 B. C. Another weight marked I found at Wroxeter was 11¼ oz., and a third of basalt, with the same mark and other mysterious characters, in Mayence museum is exactly of the standard weight.

Though more restricted in range than the bowls, the bar-currency was evidently an inter-tribal institution, both public services being apparently under the same control ; and as it is unlikely that any British chieftain had such extended powers, the only alternative is to connect both with the Druids whose power extended even into Gaul, and was the only political bond between the tribes of Britain and Ireland. Caesar, who was inti·mate with the Druid Divitiacus in Gaul, described them as students of astronomy, geography, physics (natural philosophy), and theology, to whom students flocked from Gaul to acquire the arts and sciences at head-quarters in Britain. Astronomy cannot progress without some means of measuring time, and it is remark-able that the British pattern of water-clock differs from the classical clepsydra (in which water dripped from one vessel into another) and agrees with the Hindu and perhaps the Mesopotamian system (perforated bowl from Nimrûd in Egyptian and Assyrian Dept.). There are minute directions for making water-clocks of our pattern in a Hindu manual of astronomy dating before the sixth century of our era ; but there is nothing to prove that the Druids derived it from the East, though the elder Pliny, in dealing with magic (the arts or science of the Magi), says ' it was practised with such surprising ceremonial by the Britons of his day (A. D. 23–79) that they might be thought to have instructed the Persians themselves '.

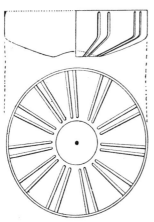

FIG. 197.—Perforated bronze bowl (with side view), Wotton. (⅙)

Archaeology has settled the true reading of Caesar's statement with regard to British currency, and his *taleae ferreae* or iron slats ' graduated according to a fixed weight-standard ' can be identified with a large series of flat iron bars with rudely shaped handles found in varying quantities at many sites in a large square district of southern England, roughly from Leominster and Northampton on the north to Bridport and Portsmouth on the Channel coast. Homer's word for a roasting-spit came to mean a coin (obol), and *drachm* was originally a handful of these thin iron rods, which appear also in the Somme Bionne burial (Cases 15, 16). The British type (fig. 198) was shaped like a sword, but quite flat with blunt edges. Since their recognition in 1905 no less than six denominations have been found, and if the Neath weight of 4770 grains is accepted as the unit, the denominations are by weight $\frac{1}{4}$, $\frac{1}{2}$, unit, $1\frac{1}{2}$ units, 2 and 4 units.

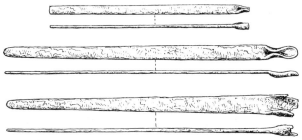

Fig. 198.—Iron currency bars (with side views) of 1, 2, and 4 units. ($\frac{1}{10}$)

PRESUMED STANDARD WEIGHTS

Denomination	Grains	Grammes	Avoirdupois.
Quarter-unit	1,192	77·4	2¾ oz.
Half-unit	2,385	154·8	5½ oz
Unit	4,770	309·7	11 oz.
Unit-and-a-half	7,155	464·6	16½ oz.
Double-unit	9,540	619·4	22 oz.
Quadruple	19,080	1,238·8	44 oz.

The most common is the double unit; and hoards of a single denomination have been found inside 'camps' (no doubt the treasure of the defenders) at Malvern, Meon Hill and Bourton-on-the-Water, Ham Hill and Hod Hill. Only two were recovered from Glastonbury lake-village, but they conform to the standard unit and double unit; and, with the series of bronze weights found at Charterhouse on the adjoining Mendips and at Melandra Castle, Glossop, confirm the above weight-system. Two unit specimens here exhibited (Case 23) are of special interest, as they had evidently been buried at the base of one of the huge jambs (now fallen) at the entrance to the stone chamber (known as Wayland's Smithy) of a long barrow in Berkshire. If they were votive offerings of money, it would seem that the well-known

M

legend dates from Early British times, though Wayland was an Anglo-Saxon hero, and later came into possession of the monument.

Though a few are recorded from the Thames at Hammersmith and Datchet, and possibly East Ham in Essex, examples are certainly rare in the south-eastern or eastern counties, the proximity of which to the Continent would account for the somewhat higher stage of culture indicated by a coinage. In the districts beyond, coins may have been unknown till Imperial times ; and the absence of currency-bars from the sites of Romano-British villages explored by Gen. Pitt-Rivers near Rushmore (under 10 miles from Hod Hill and Spettisbury) suggests that there was no overlap of iron currency and Roman coinage in that district. The maritime iron-producing district mentioned by Caesar was no doubt Sussex, where the metal was worked as recently as the eighteenth century ; and it was perhaps from this centre that the use of iron bars as currency spread through the interior of Britain.

The Early British coinage is illustrated by a few reproductions in Case 28, and more fully in the Exhibition Gallery of the Department of Coins and Medals. The earliest examples are of 'dished' or 'scyphate' form, generally with the concave face as the reverse ; and they are more or less successful imitations of the gold stater of Philip II of Macedon, who, about 356 B. C., acquired the rich gold mines of Crenides (Philippi). He died in 336, but his coins were eagerly copied by Gaulish tribes, and the type is thought to have passed to Britain about 100 B. C. The Philippus (fig. 199) weighed 133 grains, and the British series shows not only a falling-off in workmanship due to continual copying, but also a gradual diminution in weight.

A base-silver coin (plate XIII, no. 1) is placed first as being nearer a classical prototype than most, but is only distantly related to the rest. It belongs to a type common in the Channel Islands and Armorica, and British examples generally come from our south-western counties. But late specimens are said to have been found in association on more than one occasion, and Sir John Evans, who traced the evolution of the different types, classed the Channel Islands coinage as later than the gold series.

The relation between a Gaulish coin of the Bellovaci (plate XIII, no. 2) and the Philippus (fig. 199) is fairly obvious, though much has been misunderstood by the die-sinker. The obverse has the locks of hair and the laurel wreath much exaggerated, and drapery added at the neck, while the reverse has a fret-pattern in the exergue, instead of the name Philip, and only one horse is shown, the driver being placed above in the position usually occupied by a Victory on coins of Syracuse. The weight at this early stage is about 118 gr., which is reduced to 95 in the next piece illustrated (no. 3). Here the front locks of hair, the wreath, and drapery dominate the obverse ; and the charioteer on the other side is represented by pellets. The horse has become still more grotesque, and the helmet below is replaced by a pellet. On no. 4, which weighs about the same as the last, the drapery is omitted and the bandlet across the wreath exaggerated, while the limbs of the horse are separated and the head turned back. At the stage represented by no. 5 the weight is 82 or 83 gr., and the laureate head has become a cruciform pattern, the drapery at the neck still appearing below, and the transverse band becoming another wreath, while the crescent locks are placed at the centre. The reverse is better than usual, the wheel below the horse being perhaps a sacred symbol of the Gauls (p. 147), and the star with curved rays replacing the charioteer ; the wheel of the chariot still remains as a pointed oval on the left. The next (no. 6) introduces the inscribed series which, for various reasons, is considered to be, on the whole, later than the uninscribed. It is a coin of Tasciovanus, and weighs 85 gr., with the obverse derived from no. 5, which also has a somewhat similar reverse. The next type (no. 7), of 81–86 gr., is of Dubnovellaunus, a British prince mentioned on the monument erected in honour of Augustus at Ancyra in Galatia. The laurel wreath is all that remains on the obverse, and the reverse has the

FIG. 199.—Gold coin of Philip II, of Macedon. ($\frac{1}{1}$)

common ring-and-dot above the horse and a palm-branch below. The reverse of the next coin (no. 8) recalls no. 5, but also has a branch below the horse: the obverse seems to be derived from the wreath as represented on no. 7, and the weight varies from 84 to 86 gr. The specimen illustrated shows little of the lettering at the base of the reverse, but others clearly have the name Addedomaros, the final -os being the Gaulish spelling.

Owing to Roman influence, a new style was introduced ; and while the following can be safely attributed to the century between Caesar's invasion and the Claudian conquest, most of the uninscribed series must be regarded as earlier. The lettering on the obverse of no. 9 stands for Verica, while that of the reverse shows him to have been one of the sons of Commius (p. 170). The weight is 82 gr., and the vine-leaf, though conceivably evolved from the tangled lines on certain native types, was a common motive among the Romans, and occurs in glass-mosaic (Glass and Ceramic Gallery). The same may be said of the ear of corn on no. 10 (weight 81 gr.), a coin of Cunobelin struck at Colchester (*Camulodunum*). Britain exported a large quantity of corn at this time, and the wheat-ear is familiar on Greek coins of Metapontum, Lucania. Another Roman device is the eagle on no. 12, a coin of Eppillus, Verica's brother; this weighs about 18 gr., and like many other extant specimens, is meant to be one quarter of the unit weight. The reverse suggests that Eppillus was king of the Atrebates, whose capital was at Silchester (*Calleva*), though most of his coins are found in Kent. The head of Medusa seen on coins of Tincommius in the series from the sea-shore between Selsey and Bognor (Case 29) may be another Roman innovation : the legends are in Roman characters.

Another type of Verica is no. 11, the lettering on this and no. 9 being placed on opposite faces ; and the last (no. 13) should probably come early in the inscribed series, the reverse having points of resemblance to nos. 3 and 5, and the weight being 83 or 84 gr. Boduoc has not been identified, but the name occurs on a Christian tombstone at Mynydd Margam, Glamorganshire, and Boduogenus on the handle of a Roman skillet in Case D (Room of Roman

Fɪɢ. *200.—Two British coins of gold, Aylesford. ($\frac{1}{1}$)

Britain). These specimens are found in the west of England, and even in Scotland (Dumfries), and may be connected with the Dobuni of Gloucestershire.

The two gold coins (fig. 200) found on the western border of the urn-field at Aylesford (p. 127) may have been unconnected with the burials or with one another; but they help to illustrate the uninscribed British series, and belong to types represented also in Gaul. That on the left is a quarter-stater, at about the same stage of development as no. 3, the drapery showing at the neck, while the reverse is comparatively good. The other is a stater of Kentish type, the obverse being blank, as is frequently the case: the reverse is not unlike that of no. 13.

There were many other types common to Gaul and Britain, both of inscribed and uninscribed coins, some of which are exhibited in this Department ; and there were several denominations, viz. the gold stater of about 84 gr. and its quarter ; the silver piece of about 21 gr. ; and three sorts of bronze money, the normal weights of which were about 68, 34, and 17 gr. On the whole, the gold coinage was the earliest, and, as elsewhere, gradually disappeared under Roman influence, to which the silver and bronze currency must be mainly attributed. The silver was fairly pure, except in the Channel Islands coinage ; but in some cases the metal cannot be exactly determined. Besides tin, an alloy of copper, zinc, lead, and tin, called *potin*, was used, and the material called *billon* consists of about one-fifth silver to four-fifths copper.   At Hengistbury Head, besides the South-western struck type (like pl. XIII, no. 4), were found numbers of cast coins with the devices reduced to groups of dots (fork-and-pellets type) ; and these were evidently issued during the Roman occupation.

Genealogical Tables on next page]

TABLES OF ANCIENT BRITISH KINGS

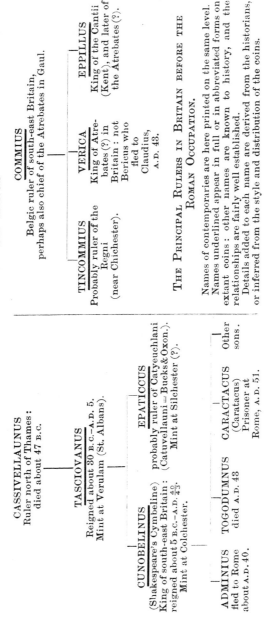

COMMIUS
Belgic ruler of south-east Britain,
perhaps also chief of the Atrebates in Gaul.

TINCOMMIUS
Probably ruler of the
Regni
(near Chichester).

VERICA
King of Atrebates (?) in
Britain : not
Bericus who
fled to
Claudius,
A.D. 43.

EPPILLUS
King of the Cantii
(Kent), and later of
the Atrebates (?).

THE PRINCIPAL RULERS IN BRITAIN BEFORE THE ROMAN OCCUPATION.

Names of contemporaries are here printed on the same level. Names underlined appear in full or in abbreviated forms on extant coins : other names are known to history, and the relationships are fairly well established.

Details added to each name are derived from the historians, or inferred from the style and distribution of the coins.

CASSIVELLAUNUS
Ruler north of Thames :
died about 47 B.C.

TASCIOVANUS
Reigned about 30 B.C.–A.D. 5.
Mint at Verulam (St. Albans).

EPATICCUS
probably ruler of Catyeuchlani
(Catuvellauni = Bucks & Oxon.).
Mint at Silchester (?).

CUNOBELINUS
(Shakespeare's Cymbeline)
King of south-east Britain :
reigned about 5 B.C.–A.D. $\frac{40}{43}$.
Mint at Colchester.

ADMINIUS
fled to Rome
about A.D. 40.

TOGODUMNUS
died A.D. 43

CARACTACUS
(Caratacus)
Prisoner at
Rome, A.D. 51.

Other
sons.

INDEX